NATIONAL LAMPOON®

Jeff Greenfield's

Book of Books

By Jeff Greenfield
With contributions by
Gerry Sussman, Sean Kelly, Ellis Weiner,
and Danny Abelson
Designed by Peter Kleinman
Edited by Sean Kelly
Distributed by Simon & Schuster

Introduction

I hereby conjure up the ghosts of lubricious fictional belles and starlets, of imaginary meat-and-potatoes gumshoes, of ultrasensitive short story adolescents and the greedy patriarchs of sagas. Of murderous make-believe paperback barbarians and the grasping, sexually repressed petits bourgeois of ten thousand novels. I summon up the spirits of vengeful, dramatically flawed heroes and the firm-breasted masochistic ingenues of romance. I conjure up the shades of windbag, butt-in do-gooders and self-serving biographers—auto- and otherwise. And I ask them all, creatures and creators: who died for your sins? And I put it to them straight: *trees,* that's who.

Whole jungles mowed down, leafy glades slaughtered, verdant oceans dried up, trunk, limb, and twig massacred, turned to pulp, turned to paper, that dull lives, dim thoughts, silly plots and tedious themes might be printed and published. (It is a fact that Britain once was entirely covered by a dense wood—the Forest Sauvage of legend. Then along came English Literature. Now look at it, hardly a sapling left....)

It grieved the heart of eco-sensitive Jeff Greenfield that yet another publishing season was coming on, and yet another tract of priceless timber was about to be sacrificed for the promulgation and marketing of interchangeable thrillers, memoirs, stroke books, tomes calculated to induce guilt feelings and tomes guaranteed to assuage them, oversized paperbacks and overpriced hard covers, slim volumes and whopping great collectors' editions.

Greenfield came to us at the *NatLamp* with the notion that if all the books about to be issued, flacked, hyped, discussed, and remaindered could be condensed and collected in a hundred pages or so, the precious natural resource of America's woodlands could be preserved. "It's a crazy idea...," we replied, "...but it just might work!"

But we knew that if we were going to scoop the *Reader's Digest*, we'd have to work fast. Agents were dispatched (in Woody Allen disguises) with the unsavory assignment of eavesdropping on other agents at Elaine's, in order to learn what the mavens of linear culture were planning. A crack research team of Herbal Essence-scented Bryn Mawr grads scanned *Publishers Weekly* for clues and portents. Greenfield himself went so far as to attend a David Obst cocktail party, wired for sound.

Within a week, we knew the loathsome intentions of every major publishing house in the nation. We were ready. Jeff's touch-typing was a thing of beauty, a flashing flame, and the page-burdened copy boy skateboarded between the Greenfield family garret and the typesetter's establishment at great speed.

Art director Peter Kleinman, over a round of ambrosiac Bloody Marys at the Illustrator's Club, enticed New York's three working design directors to describe their proposed dust jackets and typefaces, which he immediately produced for us. *NatLamp* stalwarts Abelson, Weiner, and Sussman contributed of their not inconsiderable writing talents to our project.

And here we are. Rest assured, gentle reader, that if you buy this book, you need buy no other for at least the next six months. The repentant spirit of Joyce Kilmer, poetic hypocrite whose paean to trees was written on the corpse of one, thanks you. Smokey the Bear thanks you. And so do I.

Sean Kelly

Contents

The Curse of Satan's Harvest ....*Jeff Greenfield*

Get Out of My Way or I'll Kill You ....*Jeff Greenfield*

Simply...Picasso..*Danny Abelson and Ellis Weiner*

Inscrutabilities..*Jeff Greenfield*

The Gilt-Edged Mind Rapers..*Jeff Greenfield*

The Real Adolf Hitler..*Gerald Sussman*

How Did I Get Here?...*Jeff Greenfield*

Love's Tormenting Itch...*Jeff Greenfield*

Check, Please! ....*Jeff Greenfield*

The Cooking of Provincial New Jersey ....*Gerald Sussman*

The White House Is Sinking ....*Jeff Greenfield*

The Book of Fings ....*Sean Kelly*

For $50 an Hour, I'll Be Your Own Best Friend...*Jeff Greenfield*

The Lamentation of Eve ....*Jeff Greenfield*

Poor, Schmoor! ....*Jeff Greenfield*

$1.98

The Curse of Satan's Harvest

Ethan Crowe

It was growing within her, something tiny, something terrible...possessing her body, and threatening her very life-style....

Soon could be a major motion picture!

$1.98

The Curse of Satan's Harvest

Ethan Crowe

It was growing within her, something tiny, something terrible...possessing her body, and threatening her very life-style....

Soon could be a major motion picture!

$1.98

The Curse of Satan's Harvest

Ethan Crowe

It was growing within her, something tiny, something terrible...possessing her body, and threatening her very life-style....

$1.98

The Curse of Satan's Harvest

Ethan Crowe

It was growing within her, something tiny, something terrible...possessing her body, and threatening her very life-style....

The Curse
of
Satan's Harvest

Ethan Crowe

The day had been so pleasant that Monica Anomie had almost convinced herself that it could not happen to her again.

It was just before twilight as she drove south on the Long Beach Freeway, heading home to Marina del Rey. Rush hour had passed, and the road was blissfully free of the presence of another living soul (how that phrase would return to haunt her: *"another living soul"*). The multicolored sunset began to spread out over the Pacific like a wide shot in Super 70 Panavision, while the lush scenery sped by like an establishing shot of a major motion picture.

Monica gazed at herself in the rearview mirror. She saw reflected back the face of a sensual, beautiful, intelligent, independent woman, with the quality of a Faye Dunaway, or Jane Fonda, or, depending upon contractual availability, Jill Clayburgh. Monica had been spending a part of each weekend soaking up the sun at the pool at Azygous Towers Singles Complex where she lived, and she knew that she would be the most sensual of all the women at tonight's Personal Gratification Mixer. That was important; lately, Gregg Studds had been casting an appreciative eye on the seventeen-year-old twins who lived in 23 G. She wasn't going to lose him to those...

Then it happened.

Monica suddenly felt a sharp pain slice through her stomach. Her organic lunch of bean sprouts, unpolished rice, and yogurt shake began to lurch inside her. Her car—a 1977 Caprice—suddenly began to weave back and forth across the freeway, tires squealing, in a visually and aurally exciting manner. At the last possible moment, just before the Caprice was going to crash through a barrier and plunge down a cliff into the Pacific, Monica managed to slam on the brakes and bring the car to a heartrending, dramatic stop.

Monica sat, hands trembling as they held tight to the wheel of the car, sweat pouring down her face. The pain had gone, almost as swiftly as it had come.

But the fear only grew.

What was happening to her??????

THE CURSE OF SATAN'S HARVEST

Dr. Robert Worthy leaned back in his amber leather chair, ran his lean, masculine fingers through his rich head of lustrous, chestnut brown hair, stroked the bronzed cheek of his angular, chiseled face, and rubbed his penetrating brown eyes. He bore a remarkable resemblance to Michael Douglas, or perhaps Jack Nicholson with a hairpiece, or maybe Nick Nolte or Robert Redford if they dyed their hair and wore colored contact lenses.

He should have been a contented man. At twenty-nine, Dr. Worthy had a thriving gynecological practice in Marina del Rey. His practice was netting him more than $150,000 a year, much of it in cash, enough to have brought him the real satisfactions of his profession: a lustrous brown 450 SL, a penthouse on the forty-third floor of Azygous Towers, a sixty-foot cabin cruiser. Most of the sensual young women in the singles complex chose him as their gynecologist, and the medical intimacy often led to an intimacy of a less professional but equally satisfying kind. Dr. Worthy was a master of every phase of gynecology: the prescribing of birth control pills and diaphragms and IUDs, abortions, tubal ligations, hysterectomies, and his own clitoral sensitivity enhancement treatments, which had revolutionized sexual techniques all along the Pacific Coast. There was, he seemed to remember dimly, something else that gynecologists used to do many, many years ago, but he never had learned whether that was real medicine or one of those ancient tales of witchcraft and voodoo. At any rate, Dr. Worthy had his hands full enough with all his work.

And yet...and yet...lately, something had been bothering him; nothing really dramatic, more like the foreshadowing of some incredibly exciting disaster in an especially profitable big budget motion picture by a major studio. Take this Monica Anomie: an attractive, sensual patient, who was ordinarily healthy and a prompt bill-payer. She jogged, played tennis, swam, ate natural foods, and had three to five orgasms per sexual association, well within the seventy-fifth percentile. Yet she had called for an emergency appointment, claiming only that "something wasn't quite right."

This was the fourth patient of Dr. Worthy's who had complained of something "not quite right" in the last five days.

It wasn't anything that Dr. Worthy could put his finger on (which wasn't usually the case with his patients). It was just a feeling that...something wasn't quite right.

Suddenly the telephone rang, cutting through the brief but necessary exposition. He reached for the phone and held it to his angular, masculine jawbone.

"Dr. Robert Worthy speaking," he said.

The voice on the other end of the phone was jumbled, hysterical.

"Doctor," it said, "I must see you immediately. It's...it's...*horrible!*"

"Who is this?" Dr. Worthy asked. "And what's happened?"

"It's Monica Anomie," said Monica Anomie. "And it isn't what's *happened*. It's what *hasn't* happened."

After he arranged for Monica to come over, he put the phone down and stared out of his office at the visually lush panorama. It was a look of expectation, concern, drama, and heart-pounding tension.

Something was wrong.

THE CURSE OF SATAN'S HARVEST

Paladonia Messalina first thought it was the wail of a stray cat looking for food. Strays often wandered into the alley behind the Sara Jane Moore Self-Health Collective, and Paladonia would sometimes put a bowl of milk out. Then, while the cat was drinking, she would check its sex. If it was female, she would dish out some tuna; if it was male, she would slit its throat.

Now, however, she was too busy preparing for the evening's celebrations to pay much attention to the gentle mewing of the kitten. Tonight a dozen sisters would be coming to the collective to continue their work in developing genital self-confidence, and Paladonia wanted everything to be just right. First, she prepared the candles for the ceremonial lighting of the *labia menorah*. Then she laid out the speculum at the self-cervix center.

Suddenly Paladonia looked up. The room was lit with a strange, twilight glow; shadows played on the wall in a spooky, dramatic manner, as in a big-grossing suspense movie.

The wailing outside had grown louder, more insistent.

As if gripped by some strange, uncontrollable instinct, Paladonia moved to the rear entrance and threw open the door.

It was staring up at her from the doorway.

It was...alive!

Paladonia reeled back into the room, her brain echoing with the inhuman cries from the creature as if they were on the sound track of a best-selling movie album. Somehow, through her terror, she remembered the stories she had heard years ago, stories she would hear from the old women at the market where she bought fresh basil for her pesto, stories of women's bodies horribly disfigured, of blood and gore, stories of creatures such as she was sure never existed in her safe, real life, creatures that were no part of her life, or the lives of anyone she had ever known.

And yet, there, in the doorway...the wailing...those eyes...it was alive!!!!!!!!!

"*Aaaaarrrrrrgggghhhh!*" she screamed, and crashed unconscious to the floor with dramatic suddenness.

"Well," said Dr. Robert Worthy, peeling off the rubber glove and shaking his finely chiseled masculine head as he gazed at the sensual bottom half of Monica Anomie, lying on the examining table in a manner that, depending on the angle, would draw an R or X rating from a motion picture rating board. "I'm not sure I can tell if anything's wrong."

"I *know* there's something wrong," Monica said with urgent concern in her voice. "I've never been so much as a week late before; now I'm sure I've missed my last two periods."

"Missed two periods," Dr. Worthy mused. "I've never run into a case like this in all my years here at Marina del Rey. Say," he said, in an effort to lighten the discussion, "looks like you're putting on a bit of weight around that delicious middle of yours."

"I know, Doctor," Monica said, "and I can't understand how or why. I haven't changed my diet one bit, I jog my three miles—it doesn't make any sense at all."

3

THE CURSE OF SATAN'S HARVEST

"Yes, yes," said Dr. Worthy, pacing back and forth in his examining room as the sound from his burnished, bronze-colored shoes echoed ominously off the walls. Odd, he thought, how his mind was remembering strange legends from his youth, told by withered old women who cackled and drooled as they laughed evilly, as if in some stark and eerie flashback in a first-rate, highly-grossing motion picture: legends of beings unlike any seen in Marina del Rey for all the years he could remember, beings so frightening that...no, it was impossible. His mind returned to reality.

"Monica," Dr. Worthy said, "I have to admit that I'm puzzled. What I'd like you to do is to check into a hospital for some tests. Maybe then I can figure out what's causing this odd but increasingly suspenseful and terrifying condition."

"All...all right, Doctor," Monica said, "if you think that's—*g-g-ggaaaaaggggh!*"

"Monica," said Dr. Worthy, "what's—*oh my God!*"

He watched, thunderstruck, as Monica's face turned deathly pale, tinged with a sickly, repulsive yet fascinating green. Then, without warning, she sat bolt upright as if possessed, and vomited a stream of bilious green fluid all over Dr. Worthy's Halston Megasuede laboratory coat.

"*Aaaaaarrgggh!*" Monica screamed, and slumped, unconscious, in Doctor Worthy's arms.

Jeremy Rule allowed a flicker of annoyance to pass over his normally composed face. The Quality Control Director of Kerr Laboratories had just examined the computer print-outs for the company's biggest profit-maker, the Novulate pill. The print-outs, guaranteeing the formula's purity, were always the same, month after month, and Jeremy had taken to glancing down the columns of figures and formulas with half a mind.

But today, something had caught his eye; just a number or two out of line. Probably a typographical error, Jeremy rationalized. *Except,* he knew with a terrible feeling of foreboding that could be illustrated by shadows or on the sound track, *except that computers do not make typographical errors.* He had spent two hours methodically reviewing the columns. There was no mechanical mistake. Something had gone wrong with the formula. So Jeremy Rule had waited until the other workers and executives had left. Then, quietly walking down the catwalk that led to the giant vats, Jeremy had found his way to the Novulate formula. He had scooped up a vial of the formula, and fed it into the Qualichek computer. Now, well past midnight, Jeremy was sitting in his darkened office, waiting for the computer terminal on his desk to flash the results.

His musings were interrupted by a soft knock on the door.

"You still in there, Mr. Rule?" came a rasping voice.

"Come on in, Pop," Jeremy replied, and the gnarled, white-haired night watchman shuffled into the office. Pop—nobody knew his real name—had been working at Kerr Laboratories for decades; he was probably the single most beloved person in the entire organization, and even though his usefulness as a night watchman had long since passed, he'd been kept on the payroll as a rare gesture of affection from such a bottom line organization.

"Workin' kinda late, ain't ya, Mr. Rule?" said the gentle character, so reminiscent of Barnard Hughes. "Sure hope nothin's wrong," he added politely.

"No, no, just burning the midnight oil," Jeremy said absently.

"Wouldn't be anything the matter with the Novulate formula, would it now?" Pop asked.

Jeremy looked up sharply. Pop's expression hadn't changed, and yet...and yet...was there a flicker of amusement in those rheumy old eyes?

"What do *you* know about..." Jeremy started to say. But just then the red light on his computer terminal began to flash. The results of the Novulate check were ready.

"Don't go away, Pop," Jeremy said to the old man. "I want to ask you some questions."

"Oh, don' you worry," said Pop, settling down in a chair. "I'll be right here, hee, hee, hee." His laugh sounded more like a fiendish cackle.

Quickly Jeremy tapped out the code on his desk terminal. In a flash, the video display sent back a series of letters and numbers. Jeremy read them slowly. He shook his head.

"That's impossible," he said to himself.

"Hee, hee, hee," Pop cackled.

"Must be some mistake with my instructions," Jeremy said.

"Hee, hee, hee," Pop cackled.

Twice more the laboratory executive tapped out the code. Twice more the same numbers and letters flashed back at him.

Jeremy jumped to his feet.

"No! No!" he shouted at the computer.

"Hee, hee, hee," Pop cackled.

"This isn't the formula for Novulate," Jeremy said, as if addressing an audience of lay people for whom an explanation would be necessary if they were to follow what was happening. "This is the formula for an ancient *fertility* drug: Fructovil. Why...why, any woman who took this drug would almost certainly—my God! It's impossible! In this day and age it's unheard of!"

Suddenly, Pop jumped to his feet. Gone was the sense of gnarled old man. In its place stood a figure of great strength and anger; his eyes gleamed with intelligence, will, and evil purpose.

"That's *right*, my modern young friend," Pop said, casting ominous shadows on the wall. "Did you and your ignorant compatriots think I was nothing but a dotty old man? Hee, hee, hee," he cackled, "I've been waiting years for this chance."

He wheeled to face Jeremy, whose jaw had dropped in astonishment.

"I know you know nothing of me," Pop continued. "But I was once a *doctor*—an obstetrician. Do you know what obstetricians used to do?"

"It...it rings a bell," said Jeremy, "I think we heard about it once in a course I took in folk myths. But..."

"Never mind," Pop said grimly. "You'll know soon enough. You'll *all* know. Then these pills came along; then came rock and roll music and television and frozen dinners

5

for one...and I...once a respected doctor...found myself with nothing, no work, nothing to live for.

"So I took this job and waited for my chance," Pop continued, as if in the grip of a maddened writer of additional dialogue. "First I tried a sample. Now, I've altered the entire last three months' supply. All over Southern California, nubile young women have been medicating themselves not with Novulate, but with Fructovil! Soon the world will be mine! Hee, hee, hee!!!!!"

The nurse led Dr. Worthy down the antiseptic corridor of the Temple Beth Levine Memorial Clinic and stopped at a door marked *Extremely Private*.

"She's in very bad shape, Dr. Worthy," the nurse said softly. "I can only let you see her for five minutes."

"I hope that's enough time," Dr. Worthy said grimly. "If you knew what's at stake..." He left the thought unfinished, as if hoping that a few bars of dramatic music under his words might communicate his sense of danger. How to tell the world without hurling civilization into a blind panic...the door swung open and Dr. Worthy stared at the bed, in which lay the shattered body of Paladonia Messalina.

Dr. Worthy walked over to the bed and looked down into the vacant eyes.

"Paladonia...Paladonia..." Dr. Worthy said. The pathetic figure on the bed focused upward.

"Paladonia, it's Dr. Robert Worthy," he said.

The figure stirred.

"Don't...deal with ...the patriarchal...medical..." Paladonia fell back on the bed, exhausted.

"Listen to me," Dr. Worthy said urgently. "I'm not here to debate medical procedure. You can look at each other's cervixes to your heart's content. This is much more urgent. I know that you saw something outside your clinic a week ago...something so...*horrible*, so...so *frightening*, it brought you to this state. Paladonia," he said, grabbing her shoulders and forcing her into an upright position. "I have to know what you saw. *I have to know!*"

Paladonia's eyes seemed to clear a bit. She looked at Dr. Worthy with a mixture of fear and anger, as if trying to remember and suppress her memory at the same time.

"It was...*awful*..." she began. "Smooth and...helpless and...so *small*...and yet it seemed to be compelling me to...to pick it up, to...make funny noises. Oh my *God, my God!*" She fell back once again.

"Paladonia," Dr. Worthy began, "I'm going to see somebody who may have some answers for us. She's almost a recluse now, but she used to be a teacher and a scientist. I think..." he stopped short. He had noticed a pronounced bulge under the bedcovers.

"What is that?" Dr. Worthy said, pointing to the suspicious shape.

Paladonia suddenly sounded panicked.

"It's nothing, nothing, a bulge in the bedclothes, forget it, forget—no, no, *for God's sake, don't!*"

With a sudden, angry sweep, Dr. Worthy swept the covers off the voluptuous

6

shape of Paladonia, revealing a tempting body, barely concealed by a diaphanous nightgown. There, midway between the shapely breasts and tempting mound of Venus, was the unmistakable evidence: a round ball of flesh that was once a tanned, flat belly.

"My God, Paladonia—not *you!*" Dr. Worthy exclaimed. "I've got to find out how to stop this—before it's too late!!!!!!"

The ramshackle bookstore lay on a side street several blocks inland from the tourist trails of Venice, that monument to astigmatic vision that had once inspired a developer to build a California community of seaside canals. The sun sparkled off the water as Dr. Worthy parked his car and walked through the quaint, picturesque streets, past the quaint, picturesque people who lent an air of visual interest to the late morning. It took several questions—and several generous donations of spare change—before Dr. Worthy found the Antiquarian-Fantasy Bookshop. He pushed open the door and a little bell tinkled his presence as he walked into the dusty store lined with books and cloaked in darkness.

"Anybody here?" Dr. Worthy said, looking around. "Anybody—oh!"

Looming up from behind the counter was a gray-haired crone of a woman. Her face was wrinkled like leather that had been left out in the desert sun, and she moved with the painful slowness of age.

"If'n yer lookin' fer smut, you've come to the wrong place, sonny," the old woman croaked.

"Actually," said Dr. Worthy, "I've come for some information...information that could affect the future of the entire world—*Professor O'Bairn.*"

The crone gasped, almost as if stunned by the name Dr. Worthy had spoken.

"How...how did you...how did you find..."

"Never mind that now," Dr. Worthy said. "I know that once you were one of the most respected scientists in your field...that several years ago you dropped out of sight; that no one's ever seen or heard from you since. You've got to help me." He withdrew from his Calvin Klein sport coat a piece of drawing paper and thrust it at her.

"These...*creatures* have begun appearing here in Southern California. If word gets out, it could throw the entire media market into absolute pandemonium. I've got to know if they're some horrible figment of the imagination or if...they're real."

The old woman slowly unfolded the piece of paper. She stared at the drawing for a long, dramatically fulfilling moment. Then she glanced back up at Dr. Worthy, nodding slowly, solemnly.

"Real?" she said, laughing humorlessly. "*Real?* I'll tell you how real they are. *Three* of them lived in my home. For years. I stopped counting long ago." She shut her eyes, as if blotting out the memory.

"It didn't seem that bad at first—they were so small, I mean. But then I realized what their diabolical scheme was all about...the screams in the night...the smell in their rooms...the way they made us prisoners in our own home...no time for *play,* no time to *work,* no time for *love,* no time to *think*...they took over our lives...."

She lowered her voice.

7

"Do you know what else they do?" she whispered, still recalling the terror within her mind.

"They live off the flesh of young women!"

"Now really," Dr. Worthy said, "I don't believe..."

"That's right," the crone said sarcastically. "That's right, don't believe. I know—look at my body. Years and years, every day, yielding to their insatiable hunger for my own juices. *Look at me!"* she screamed. "Do you know how old I am? *I'm thirty-one years old. They did this to me!*

"That's why I dropped out of sight," she continued, "and that's why I came here. Every study I'd made of Southern California convinced me that there was no way such life could survive in this climate. And for years I thought I'd been proven right."

Dr. Worthy looked at her imploringly.

"Please, Professor O'Bairn," he said. "You must help me. The future of our way of life-style as we know it is at stake. What can be done?"

Professor O'Bairn looked away for a moment. Then she began to speak with the low, soft tone of absolute urgency.

"There is one possible antidote," she said. "This is what you must do...."

She continued speaking, without pause, for more than two hours.

Monica Anomie turned off the Long Beach Freeway as the glorious Southern California day was turning into the glorious Southern California sunset. On her car radio, Donna Summer's "Livin' It, Livin' It, Livin' It" was fading from the speaker, and the opening sounds of the Village People's "Such Interesting People Live on Christopher Street" was becoming audible. She pulled into the parking space at Dr. Robert Worthy's office and hurried inside, where Dr. Worthy and Paladonia Messalina were tapping their feet in time to the rhythm of "Disco Inferno."

"Well, well, well," said Dr. Worthy, "how's our patient today?"

"Just fine, thanks," said Monica. "I'm going dining tonight at Duke Humphrey's, and then there's a dance party at the Lone Hand."

Paladonia smiled happily.

"It's a miracle, Dr. Worthy," she said. "I don't know how you figured it out."

"It was really Professor O'Bairn," Dr. Worthy said modestly. "After listening to her, I realized that the Southern California climate wasn't enough to drive the creatures away. We need radical doses of something so alien to their survival that they'd just vanish. The answer was right in front of our eyes—or ears."

"Disco," said Paladonia.

"Right," said Dr. Worthy. "In proper doses, disco builds up an absolute invulnerability to these...life forms."

"But Doctor," said Monica. "Isn't it possible that over time, these creatures will find a way to build up resistance? Might they not surface yet again?"

Dr. Worthy looked off into space, as if gazing at a huge, unseen audience.

"I don't know, Monica," he said grimly. "I think it's too early to tell whether any of us will live to see *The Curse of Satan's Harvest II.*"

Do Hans Stricker's theories work? We can testify firsthand that they do.

From the moment Hans Stricker walked into our office with his arresting opening statement—"Don't nobody move!"—we knew we were in the presence of a uniquely captivating individual, with a message especially suited to today's times, when everyone wants to make the most of his opportunities. So powerful were his arguments, so compelling the manner in which he presented them, that we overrode our long-standing editorial policy and decided to publish *Get Out of My Way or I'll Kill You*. As one editor put it, "Maybe we don't take stuff over the transom, but when it comes through your window, well, that's another story. I've got three kids."

We don't really know too much about Hans Stricker, and, as he put it, "It's a lot healthier that way." But we feel confident in saying that here an old publishing cliché is true: once you pick up this book, you won't be able to put it down.

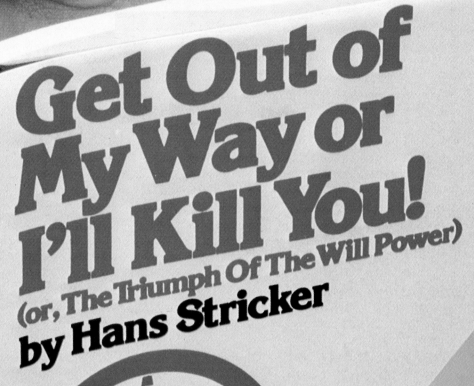

Get Out of My Way or I'll Kill You!

(or, The Triumph Of The Will Power)

by Hans Stricker

HOW TO GET WHAT YOU WANT FROM PEOPLE BY PLAYING THE GAME CALLED "WINNING"

BLITZKRIEG PRESS

1

Get Out of My Way
Or
I'll Kill You

How It Works

Hey!

You! The fish-faced one, over there by the Recent Titles section of the bookstore!

Yeah! Hey, don't look up or you're in big trouble!

That's it, that's it, just keep reading this page, nice and easy like, and maybe nobody will get hurt. Now, don't look up, but I'm standing right over there...uh-uh, don't look up, now....Anyway, I'm standing there, and I'm giving you a friendly little piece of advice. If you don't buy this book—*right now*—I'm going to follow you out of this store until I get you when you're all alone and defenseless. And then I'm going to jump on top of you and beat you into a bloody pulp with my fists and maybe crack a few ribs, as well as violate one or more of your bodily goddamn orifices, if you get my drift.

Now, maybe you don't believe me. Am I right? I mean, after all, there's thousands of bookstores in this country, and I can't be in them all, right? Only —hey, *keep your eyes on the page!*—if you happen to guess wrong...I mean, if I *am* standing over there in the corner...and if I *do* follow you out the door... well, the next few hours are not exactly going to be the most pleasant you've ever known.

So be a good person, and just to be on the safe side, walk slowly over to the cash register—don't look around, now—give the man the money for the book, and while you're at it, tell him to order a couple more, because you're going to be picking up a few copies for your friends. Then, when the book is paid for and all wrapped up, you can go home, unwrap it again, and start finding out how you can put the simple techniques I've demonstrated here to work for *you*.

*"Are you sure I'm not watching you?...
Wanna take a chance or buy the book?"*

How It Was Born

Six years ago, I was a loser.

Let me amend that. I was a *loser's* loser.

I worked in a shoe store in downtown Chicago. Eleven hours a day, I was down on my knees, trying to squeeze pairs of size ten feet into pairs of size eight shoes, and the *smell*—forget it. And for all of it, you know what I took home every week? A big fat ninety-six dollars and forty-seven cents. My boss was a fat guy named Barkewicz, who was always ordering me around, telling me, "Could you please wait on this customer?" and really insulting stuff like that. And if all that wasn't bad enough, he used to bring his daughter to the store all the time, and people would keep tripping over her crutches and everything.

Well, one day, as we were closing up, Barkewicz was standing by the cash register counting the day's receipts when the simple idea that was to change my life—and may soon change yours—jumped into my head. I looked at my paycheck—the same goddamn ninety-six dollars and forty-seven cents—and then I looked into the cash register, where there must have been four hundred dollars.

Barkewicz had more than four times as much money as I had. If I could get his money, I'd be four times as happy as I was without it. So I had to choose between his happiness and mine. But since *he* was already looking out for *his* happiness, *I* had to look out for *my* happiness. *I had to take the responsibility for my own fate.*

The rest was simple. I jumped over the counter, pushed Barkewicz against the wall, scooped all the cash out of the register into my pocket, and told him that if he so much as breathed a word of this to the cops, then no matter how long it took, I'd find his daughter and break every unwithered bone in her body.

As I sauntered casually from the store with four hundred dollars in cash in my pocket—as well as a check for ninety-six dollars and forty-seven cents—I remember thinking that a huge, black cloud had passed out of my mind, leaving me with a clear vision of the future.

I had found it.

And now I'm going to help you find it, too.

What Is It?

My idea, the key to happiness, first took shape in that shoe store. It's a theory I like to call the *Cookies in the Playpen* theory.

This theory cuts through the fog of guilt-inducing hang-ups that the authority figures in your life have settled over your head. It takes you back to the primal state of your childhood, and asks you to imagine that you and five other toddlers are playing in a playpen. O.K.? Can you feel the cuddly, warm bodies of the other little children? Can you feel the clammy, wet diapers? Good. Now imagine a grown-up comes by and puts a plate of six cookies in the playpen.

As the grown-up walks away, she says to you and your little playmates, "Now I want you to share, children; there's one cookie for each of you."

Now—before the hang-ups, before society's juvenile offender authorities get a hold of you—what do you, that child in the playpen, think?

Do you think: "Goody-goody, one cookie for each of us!"?

Do you think: "I only really want one cookie"?

Bushwa, pal! What you think is: "*I want every one of those f------ cookies!*" And if there were no grown-ups around, you'd pummel the living pardonmyfrench out of every one of those kids and eat all those cookies yourself!

The only reason you don't is because you're afraid: afraid your parents might come in and punish you—like mine would do—by tying you up and throwing you in a closet or holding your hands over a hot stove.

Remember?

Well, here's the key to taking responsibility for your own happiness:

Right now, if you're over twenty-one, you can probably beat the living p--- out of your old man or old lady. Really. Look at them sometime. Look at those flabby arms, those spindly legs, the gray hairs poking out over that spavined chest. Now look at your own body: the muscles rippling down your arms; the pecs bulging through your T-shirt.

Do you get It? Do you see those cookies, all sweet and crunchy, lying there in the playpen? Do you see your weak, pathetic parents, sitting on their rocking chairs? Okay, baby: *go get those cookies!*

Painting a positive mental portrait.

3

How to Paint a Mental Portrait of Your Victory

Even though you may understand It now, it's not going to be easy to translate theory into action. If you've been one of life's losers all these years, no single insight is going to change you into a winner. Because in your mind are all those guilt-inducing figures you've been dragging through your past. You know the kind of figures I'm talking about: your truant officer, your psychiatric evaluator, your court-appointed lawyer, your section guard...familiar figures to me, and, I'm sure, to you.

Now the only way to get rid of these figures—to "knock the bastards off," as I like to put it—is to replace them with other mental portraits in your own mind. These portraits will give you the confidence to put the theories into action...to "get those cookies."

It's important first thing to make the portraits as firm and powerful as possible. Maybe you've gone to some so-called assertiveness training program where you've been taught to look at some powerful figure and imagine him in his underwear.

Not good enough, buddy. *Not nearly good enough.*

When *I'm* dealing with powerful people, I like to imagine them tied up, gagged, and naked in the trunk of my car.

Or I imagine myself pointing a powerful "persuader" at them, like one of my 30.06s, with them cowering at my feet, begging for mercy, while I'm laughing my head off at them and making them get up and bark like a dog or cluck like a chicken, while they empty their pockets and give me all their money and get off their goddamn high horses with their fancy talk about "psychomotor personality disorder" and...like that.

Or say there's a really special girl you want to nail, if you get my drift. But somehow you feel you just aren't good enough to even ask her to dinner, much less slip her the goods, if you're on my wavelength.

Your problem can be solved if you just get the right mental portrait in your head. For example, imagine this bimbo in a cheap fleabag motel, with the M-O-T-E-L sign blinking on and off, and she's lying on this cruddy bed, all naked, and some guy is slipping it to her, if you're following me, and she's thrashing around, and kicking, and moaning, and salivating, and her eyes are rolling up into the back of her head, and she's heaving and bucking and just acting like an animal....See, the great thing about this mental portrait is that you'll probably be so disgusted thinking about all this, you won't even want to go near her; so if she says no to you, it's no loss.

Now let's try to see how another mental portrait can help you get what you want out of life. Let's suppose you're trying to make some big sale to some big corporation. You go into their offices, and it's a big building, and the lights are bright, and you're getting one of those terrible headaches that we've all been getting since we were little kids, and there's like a big siren going off inside your head and it feels so terrible....

Anyway, I like to imagine that this big corporation is a small family living in a thatched roofed hut somewhere in Europe, and I'm this big tank, like one of those World War II German babies. Then I picture myself rolling right up to the house, and right through the front door, and all the people inside are screaming and yelling and begging me to stop, and they're thrashing about and kicking and moaning, but the tank just keeps on *rolling* and knocking everything *down,* and there's smoke and fire—bright, warm fire—and then all of a sudden all of the screaming stops. . . .

Pictures like these in your head can make all the difference. They can turn you from a loser into the kind of winner who will get what he wants when he wants it.

Getting their attention.

Verbal Ransom Notes to
Get What You Want

These mental portraits are very useful. But of course you can't communicate these portraits to the people you're dealing with. It's not just that they can't see what's inside your mind, despite all the fancy theories of the people who make you go into their offices and lie down on couches and talk about what's in your mind. It's that if you tried to tell some of these people about what's inside your mind, they'd get all the wrong ideas, and try to give you pills and stuff to make the pictures go away.

When you're dealing with people—in business, in love, in trying to get them to turn their radios and TVs down,which always make so much noise that they give you terrible headaches and everything's *noisy* and *too loud*—you have to know how to talk to them in language they will *understand* and *respect*. In my studies of human communication, I've discovered that the most efficient and response-generating communication is the *ransom note*.

Think about it for a minute: you want something from some snooty guy who lives in a big house with fancy china and wears suits and ties. What happens if someone like you calls him up? You kidding me? You're lucky if the goddamn butler or maid will take the message. Am I right, or what?

Now, let's say you know which way their kid gets home from school, and one day you sort of walk along the same route and there's the kid, little Miss Snooty, so you invite the kid in for a soda, and then you bring the kid back to your room, and you take some cut up magazines and put a note together and the note reads: *If you want to see Jessica* (they always name the kid some goddamn thing like Jessica), *put $5,000 in a shoebox and leave it by the mailbox at State and Lake.*

I promise you, Mr. and Mrs. Snooty will read *that* note, all right.

This is the technique that can make the difference in your own life. You have to learn the subtle techniques of delivering *Verbal Ransom Notes,* to let the people you're dealing with know you mean *business.*

Now let's break these kinds of communications into their component parts:

1. *Getting Their Attention:* No matter what kind of transaction you're trying to undertake, you first have to get the attention of the other party, or, as I like to think of him, the *Victim.* (Remember: if you're not the Perpetrator, you're the Victim. It's up to you.) Maybe it's a sale you're trying to make, or a woman, if you catch my hint. O.K. You need a good, attention-getting opener. For instance, "Hey—you talking to me?" Or, "If you want this apartment burned to a crisp, then don't open this door." These are what I call *Forcing Gambits,* since they require some response, like "Huh?" or, 'Martha, you call the police.''

2. *Clarifying the Transaction:* You can't expect to get what you want from any enterprise unless you make clear what you want: fifty thousand dollars, a new color TV, the Sudetenland, whatever. So once you've got their attention, you have to set down the transaction as you understand it. This can be done directly ("Give me that coat or I'll rip your arm off your body") or indirectly ("Which would you rather have—that coat or your left arm?"). Either way, you've made your proposition clear.

3. *Overcoming Objections:* In any endeavor, you're more than likely to find objections from the other party, or Victim. This is because nobody wants to do you any favors. It's always that way, if you think back to your own past, when people wouldn't let you play with them or go to parties at their house or borrow their records or anything, and you were always alone, day after day, in that terrible, small, dark, smelly room where you first got those terrible headaches, and the noise like a great big siren going off in your head hour after hour and it just won't stop.

Let's say you've gotten their attention and clarified the transaction. The objections will start coming the moment the nature of the transaction is understood. You have to be aware at all times in order to pick up the clues that an objection is being raised. Phrases like, "You'll never get away with this," or, "Martha, you call the police" are good indications that not all is well with the transaction.

There are both verbal and nonverbal methods you can use to overcome these kinds of objections: stand in front of the door with your arms folded across your chest, take a rubber truncheon out of your back pocket, and slap it rhythmically into your palm. Rip a major metropolitan telephone book in half. Or, if you're the verbal type, try these powerful phrases:

"What's your life insurance company?"

"Oh, a wise guy, eh?"

"You talkin' to me?"

4. *Holding the Power Position:* Body language, as I've told you already, and you better be listening up good if you know what's good for you, is a key to getting what you want. As you move toward a completion of the transaction, it can be even more important.

One good power position is to stand up while your adversary, or Victim, is lying face down on the floor with his hands tied behind his back, and let's see whether he'll be as high-and-mighty now as he was when you first approached him and maybe your clothes weren't as good as his and maybe you didn't talk as good or didn't use the right knife and fork and all. . . .

Another good power position involves a direct application of a well-known psychological device called *closure.* I'm not sure exactly what it means in those big fat books that are in the guy's office they make you go to, but here's how I use it: I get real close to the guy I'm dealing with, and I take his arm in my hand, and I kind of bend it behind his back. This is really effective, especially when the guy's real *old* and like that.

Establishing a power position.

7

6

A Sample Dialogue

How does this technique work in practice? Let me give you a sample of a typical transaction. I'll keep it simple because right now you're probably the type who's scared to take a book out of the library. Let's say you want a nice meal, but you don't have cash because the people at the welfare office don't want to give money to people whose skins you can see in the dark, if you see what I'm driving at. Here's how to get what you want. We'll call you the Perpetrator, and the guy behind the counter the Victim.

Perpetrator: *(Sits down at the counter)* Hey, anybody working here?

Victim: Help you, buddy?

Perp: You talking to me? *(Getting Their Attention)*

Victim: Sure, what can I do. . .

Perp: *(Grabbing victim by collar, pulling him down to counter, establishing a Power Position)* You can stop calling me buddy for openers if you don't want your face smashed into a bloody pulp. *(Getting Attention, con't.)*

Victim: S-sure, s-sure, what do you want, sir?

Perp: Eggs easy over, sausage, large o.j., and thirty-five bucks in cash. *(Clarifying the Transaction)*

Victim: Say, what is this, a stick-up or something? *(Objection)*

Perp: Of course not, fella. It's a loan. I'm your buddy, ain't I? You called me buddy, didn't you? *(Grabbing his arm, bending it behind his back in Power Position II; also Overcoming Objection)*

Victim: Right, right, sure thing, sure thing.

Now suppose you're saying to yourself, "It looks fine on paper, but it doesn't work in real life."

Well, I'm telling you it does. Maybe you want to have an argument about it, right? Maybe you want to go outside and settle this like men, huh? Maybe I'm standing outside your door right now, ready to break it down and find out if you're reading this and laughing at me like all those other people who some-how never made it home, right? Well, you just go out and try these things, and see if it doesn't do for you what it did for me. You'll do all right. Believe me.

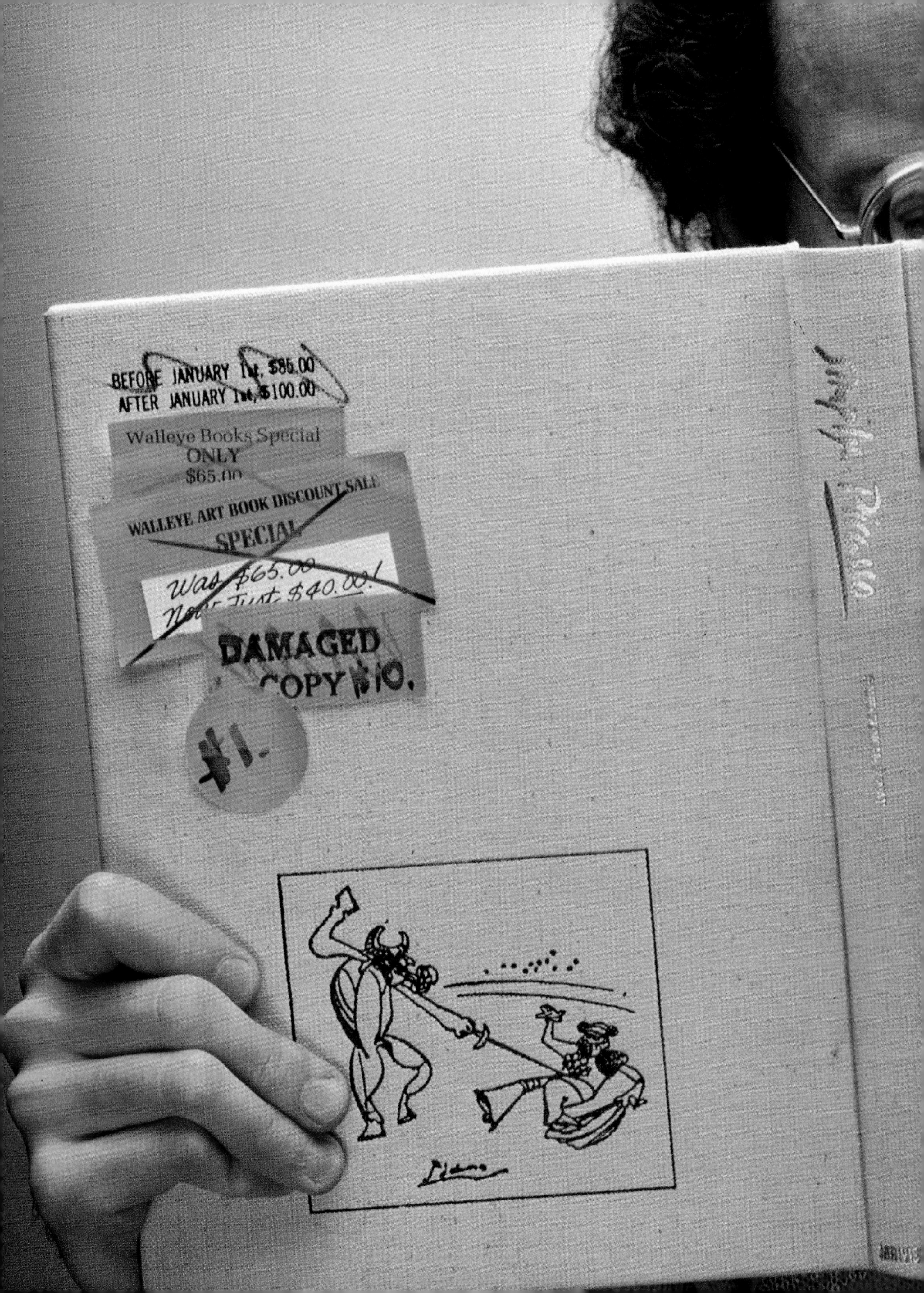
BEFORE JANUARY 1st, $85.00
AFTER JANUARY 1st, $100.00
Walleye Books Special
ONLY
$65.00
WALLEYE ART BOOK DISCOUNT SALE
SPECIAL
Was $65.00
Now Just $40.00!
DAMAGED
COPY $10.
$1.

simply...Picasso

DAVID DUNCAN DONAT

Simply...Picasso

Some have called him "the most wonderful person who ever lived." Others insist he is more important than everybody else in the world put together. To me, he is simply . . . Picasso.

This book began five years ago, towards the end of my work on *My Best Pal Pablo* (Viking, $49.95). Picasso had turned to me from his canvas, his face set in a brooding mask of concentration, the golden Mediterranean light slanting across the studio floor, and said, "In a world of confusion, only the image has clarity."

At that moment, this book was born.

D. D. D.

Picasso's Statement to the Author

David — I must say nothing. Like me, you are a man. These are photographs. You took them. To truth!

Picasso

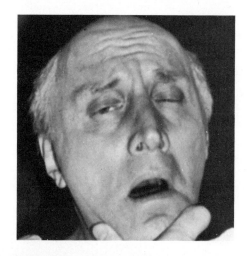

Edmondo the rooster heralds the dawn to a sleepy household. "El es mi alarm clock," says Picasso, who traces a fondness for early rising to his peasant ancestry.

The Picasso table is a meeting place for friends and well-wishers from the world over. This morning the Great One is host to three countrymen, delegates from a Spanish Civil War Veterans' Organization, who have come, like so many others, in search of patronage for their cause.

A discovery! A trinket created for the delight of children seizes Picasso's imagination.

The creative flame that burns within flares anew. The convivial murmur around him recedes; the powerful hands knead and shape. He freely transforms the ordinary into the extraordinary, as with sure, economical motions, he enlists these mundane materials in the service of his genius.

Art and Life meet.

In the sultry Provence afternoon, Picasso ascends to the studio. Here, his artistic spirit rules supreme; nothing must disturb the rising ferment of his creative essences. For hours he paints furiously, his inspiration gushing forth in a lava-like eruption of fertile energies. It is late afternoon when the beautiful Jacqueline pays him a discreet visit, sharing a tender moment with the man whose privacy she guards so devotedly.

Picasso's pleasure at a gift from Manolete is evident as he gestures to the gods in the traditional manner, the thunderous roars of the *corrida* ringing in his ears. The ceremonial garb stirs deep emotion within the maestro. More than merely a favorite subject, bullfighting is this Spaniard's metaphor for the Great Struggle. Maturity has not robbed Picasso of the ability to enter, childlike, into other worlds.

A delighted Claude becomes *el toro* to Picasso's matador. Showing a solemnity befitting this moment of truth, he is no longer a child, but a combatant in an ancient contest in which one or the other must die.

*Dusk: Portrait of
the Artist in Repose*
Picasso surveys
the day's accomplishments as his
wife looks on.

Inscrutabilities

MELVIN MEGO

WINNER OF THE COVETED
PRIX TENTIOUS

Here—as a humbly grateful literary community bows its head with thanks—is the novel we have been anticipating for decades, a work that at once sweeps away the cobwebbed conventions of the twentieth century novel and erects, on its own foundation, a monument to stand as the paradigm of what we will someday come to call the "Mego Novel."

In story and characterization—for those who cling to such security blankets—*Inscrutabilities* is deceptively simple, almost vague. Tom Noddy sits in his office, in a department (perhaps English?) of a small, out-of-the-way college, contemplating his fate. He surveys his office, and, by extension, his life—and ours. Formless, neochaotic, Noddy's rumination—at once Proustian and Joycean, yet cast of its own mold—takes him to childhood, first love, first sorrow, the wrenching agony of his struggle to find a foundation granting him security in his life—and a battle for tenure that recalls the most intense of Stephen Crane.

With a remorseless refusal to surrender to the insatiable demands of a pap-fed generation of readers, Mego instead throws down a gauntlet. "This is *art,*" his novel seems to challenge us, "art at the highest of peaks, where the air is thin, the pathway treacherous, the footholds nonexistent. Follow me only if you dare to think yourself worthy of the journey."

In such pride—arrogance, if you will—is literature's future, art's purpose, mankind's hope.

At thirty-nine, Melvin Mego stands as one of the most widely heralded writers under forty in the American literary-academic community. Fragments of his long-awaited first novel first appeared in 1959, in the *Sewannehowilovya Review,* and critics immediately acclaimed Mego as "an astonishingly promising under-twenty genius."

In 1967, his 800-word character sketch in *Bavardage Quarterly* caused Edmund Wilson to dispatch a 500-word mailgram calling Mego "among the most noteworthy of our under-thirty writers." In 1975, portions of a first draft of the book jacket of *Inscrutabilities* triggered a storm of controversy in the prestigious literary magazine *Caviar to the General.* "Unsurpassed potential among writers under thirty-five," was the judgment of Christopher Lehman-Brothers.

Mr. Mego has established his literary reputation without sacrificing his academic career. A graduate of Southampton College, Mr. Mego has an M.A. from Yale, a D.B. from Helmsley-on-Thames, a D.Litt. from Rockefeller University, and a *Dos Equis* from the Institute of Puerto Vallarta. He has received a Guggenheim, a Ford, a Fairchild, and a Wasserman. He is currently at work on the pagination of his doctoral thesis at the University of Aspen under that school's pioneering Scholar-in-Nonresidence program.

Mr. Mego divides his time among Aspen, Sag Harbor, and Brooklyn Heights. He lives with Carole Trelawny, the noted consumer.

"I would sooner admit to criminal assault on a blind, ninety-year-old double amputee than confess my failure to read this masterpiece. It is compulsory for all who would claim to grasp the essence of postnuclear man."

Harold deBoer, Editor
Bavardage Quarterly

"One of those rare works which, like Galileo's telescope or Darwin's thesis, alters our fundamental perception of the universe. It is as if all we have seen and heard has been touched by the brushstroke of genius. It is, I suppose, possible to live without reading Inscrutabilities, *but why would one wish to?"*

Oscar Baragouin

"Were it not for the outmoded command of the Constitution, I would prowl the streets at night, break down doors, and force my fellow citizens to read this book at gunpoint."

Brenda Shagetz Eisenstein

"An evocative myth as allegory."
Philip Rahv

"A stunning allegory as myth."
Ravi Shankhar

"Haunting...evocative...stunning."
Albert Shanker

"Not to read this book is to forfeit one's membership in the community of civilized mankind."
Prof. Irwin Snitow
Associated Chairperson, English Department
Bronx Community College

INSCRUTABILITIES

Book One—Agape

Testament the First—1964–1966

Chapter I

1.

Tom Noddy in his office.

It was as if he contained his office within him, even as his office contained him within itself. And it was of himself within itself as well.

The desk into which his soles had worn a depression as deep as the depression within his soul seemed to encompass in its solidity, its stolidity, his own insensate essence.

The test sheets, fresh from the mimeograph machine down the hall—how near, he thought, with evocative, acute irony, *hall* is to *hell*—smelled of pungent chemicals, felt of the slick viscosity of an eighteen-year-old coed who had exchanged priapic entry for academic spoils. He had had her orifice in his office, had Noddy. *Nymph. in thy orifice. be all my sins dismembered.*

Noddy sighed. What could one make of that of sigh? What could one make of that sigh if, seeking to fill a book with the experience of a man who did nothing, one needed to make of that sigh an epiphany?

Well, then. Perhaps it was a sigh one might make at a faculty club, over a hand of bridge, when one finds oneself playing a slam bid where one's partner is void in trumps. *A sigh of bridge.* Noddy thought, wondering if those who bid such a bid were no brighter than those who bid on subsidiary rights, who would surely understand the haunting, evocative reference to Venice. *Venice Rome. do as the Romans do.* The pun died. Death in Venice. *A Mann's a mann for a' that.*

It was a sigh one might make at the end of winter, when spring had not yet come. *Beware the sighs of March.*

To Tom Noddy, spring meant more than *shoures soote* and the only pretty ring time. For thirty of his thirty-six years, schoolboy, undergrad, scholar and teacher, spring signified end of term. Coming to term. Release, however temporary, from the womb of academe. To watch the wet marks left by the childrens' bathing suits dry slowly on the concrete poolside, and think about the play. His own, his demon, his never-to-be-produced work of genius. there. typed. penciled. ballpoint-scarred. all first hundred pages of it in his desk. His gift. He could see in his mind's eye. Horatio its title typed. in fantasy lights, in headlines of *Erewhon* by Tom Noddy *la casa stесть.*

Since before the drama department. and the faculty meetings. and the station wagon. and the pool. and the kids. for .... Noddy ...... his demons. happily. while his las still ....

Tom cast a .... blue lagoon ....

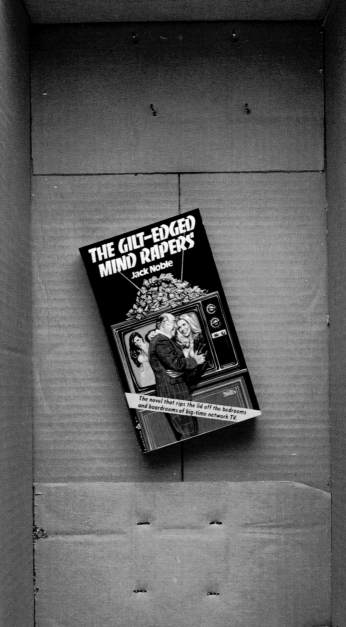

PROLOGUE

The sun is warm here on the island of Penang, off the Coast of Malaysia. So is the sand and sea; so is the body of Kathy, my beloved, who's now inside our little hut, preparing our midday meal of delicious Malaysian food: tropical fish, fruit, and cheese.

It's a good life, I suppose, even though I don't know how long they'll let me live. But when I think back to just a few short weeks ago, to my plush existence as a $400,000-a-year program executive with one of America's major TV networks; when I think of the luxury, the power—and above all, of the horrible, monstrous conspiracy that lay beneath the tinsel and the platinum—it's almost too much to believe.

Yet it's true—all of it. And this is my attempt to tell you what I've learned, so that we can stop this mind-boggling scheme before it's too late. Yes, just a few short weeks ago I began to learn about it. Yes, just a few...short...weeks...ago....

I

The early morning New York sunshine slanted into the penthouse, gleaming off the Baccarat champagne glasses that stood on the Bokhara rug that lay in the master bedroom of my sixteen-room duplex penthouse atop one of Sutton Place's older luxury buildings.

"Mmmmmmm," came the throaty growl of the luscious honey blonde with tanned skin, erect breasts, and a hard, round behind who called herself Cindy—they're all named Cindy or Vicky, I've noticed. She sinuously wriggled out from under the blue satin sheets.

"Oooooohhhhhh, *Jack*, that was...*incred*ible," she whispered, licking my ear. "Was it really a dozen times?"

"Mmmmmm," I murmured, feeling the warm sense of arousal building again in my groin. "And you don't believe that nonsense about thirteen being bad luck, do you?"

Cindy giggled her approval and mounted me for another joyride. Soon she was approaching her climax, writhing and moaning, "Oh, my God, Jack, you're so big, you're so thick, you're so deep, you're so masterful, ohhhhhhh...." She collapsed onto my chest, all but unconscious with total joy and satisfaction.

I chuckled indulgently, and patted her hard, round behind as I jumped into the shower-sauna-gym-racketball court and then dressed quickly—Turnbull and Asser shirt, H. Huntsman suit, Lobb shoes. "I'd love a rematch," I said, "but right now there's some hard-nosed business to attend to."

I buzzed downstairs, and by the time I'd finished the forty-floor ride in my private elevator with the four screen TV console, my Bentley was waiting to speed me to the midtown headquarters of Transnational Broadcasting Company—and a rendezvous with an unbelievable destiny.

1

II

As I strode through the marble and glass lobby of the Transnational Broadcasting Company, two college-age kids cornered me.

"Aren't you Jack Wellborn, vice-president of prime time programming, East Coast, of TBC?" one of them asked.

"Guilty," I quipped.

"We just want to tell you," the other said, "that we still think 'The Young Porpoises' was the grooviest program that ever was, and we want you to keynote the Fifth Annual Porpoise Convention. We drew 15,000 'Porpies' last year," he said with pride.

"I'll see what I can do," I said, but there was a lump in my throat as I rode the executive elevator up to my sixty-eighth floor office. "The Young Porpoises" had been my baby; I mother-henned that show from conception through development through a script-by-script shaping into a show that I feel had a little something to do with making people hate each other a little less. Some observers still think it was a special showing of "The Young Porpoises" that stopped a war in Central America with its simple message that "it takes all kinds of people—and other living things—to make a better world." All I knew was that it could have been bigger than "Star Trek." And then, Fred Golderman, senior programming vice-president, canceled the show—and no one knew why. Oh, he sugarcoated me with the new title, the salary, the office, the vacations, the cars, the stock options; but he never said why he'd taken that show off the air.

* * *

"Jack, Jack!" Angie interrupted my reverie as I walked past the Klee and the De Kooning into my four-room suite of offices with six TV sets, four cassette players, squash court, Jacuzzi, hot tub, and water bed. Angie was my efficient, good-humored, and thoroughly luscious thirty-four-year-old secretary-researcher, hangover-curer, and bodyguard. She had no life of her own; frankly, she was completely devoted to me and to a certain portion of my anatomy. I couldn't believe she never shared her hard, lean body with anyone else—but she'd often told me that once a month with me was better than twice a night with any other man in the world. Now she seemed terribly upset.

"What happened, Angie?" I inquired.

"Please—please," she gasped. "First, I need it so bad." Angie collapsed to the floor, groping for my zipper; soon she had my hard masculinity in her fist, and was guiding it into her sweet, luscious mouth. She had a tongue and lips like a Shower Massage, and I came like Old Faithful. She greedily swallowed every drop.

"Now," I said, straightening my clothes. "What is it you're so upset about?"

"It's—it's Mike Donne, senior development vice-president, and one of your closest friends," she sobbed. "He's—*dead!*"

III

"But who—how—where?"

A voice from behind me, unctuous, soothing, yet somehow ominous, said, "I can explain, Jack."

The voice belonged to Fred Golderman, thirty-four-year-old compulsive, ruthless, ambitious programmer. With Donne's death, Golderman would take over the top programming job at TBC. As Golderman gestured, the light shone off his solid gold lapel pin, tie tack, and cuff links, all with the number "100." Golderman had never explained the meaning of this symbol.

"Donne was waiting for an elevator," Golderman said, "and somehow fell into an open shaft."

"That's silly," I said. "Those elevators are foolproof. Besides, Donne told me he was onto something important about some kind of...of...*conspiracy* that—"

"Never mind that," Golderman said, cutting me off with a wave of his hand. I could swear a thin bead of sweat formed over his lip: Golderman *never* sweated.

* * *

As Golderman left my office, the buzzer on my intercom rang. It was Angie.

"It's Walter Krankit, grizzled news chief and a veteran of the Murrow-Friendly era of hard-boiled professional news," she said. "He'd like to come in for a minute."

"Send him—hold it," I said as a feminine giggle under my desk told me Krankit would have to wait a few minutes. For hiding under my desk was his daughter, nineteen-year-old Fiona Krankit; the Wellesley sophomore, here on an internship, had developed an absolutely animalistic attraction for me. She lived for sex the way a lion lived for antelope meat. Now she was crouched, face down, her Diane von Furstenberg dress hiked to her armpits, her bikini panties around her ankles.

"Put it where I like it best, Jack," Fiona moaned, and I obliged.

"Oh," she gasped, "it's so tight, it's so—ooooohhhhhhh," and she came, bucking and thrashing all over my Karastan carpet.

"Now, get out quick—the back way," I whispered, patting her hard, round behind.

"That's the way I like it, Jack," she giggled. Fiona was barely out the door when her father, Walter Krankit, burst in, waving a sealed envelope.

"Jack," he said grimly, "when you see this—you won't believe your eyes!"

IV

"You don't think I'm off the wall, do you, Jack?" asked Krankit.

"Hell, no, Walter," I said. "You were gofering for Murrow in the middle of the Blitz—you researched his McCarthy exposè; you're crusty, hell, yes, but damn it, you've got some com*mit*ment, some hu*man*ity."

"All right," Krankit said grimly. "Just before Donne took that last elevator ride, he told me he'd stumbled on a page from Fred Golderman's secret diary. He gave me the page in a sealed envelope and told me to open it only if he died in the TBC building under suspicious circumstances."

I slit the envelope open, and we looked together at the page from Golderman's secret diary with disbelieving eyes. *Dallas, November 22, 1963* (it read). *All set. Get dough to L.H.O. and other gunmen. Tell Zapruder 12:30 P.M. is go time. Point camera directly opposite grassy knoll. Sign contract at 1:03 P.M.*

"Can you possibly figure out what this means?"

"Well," I mused, "it seems that Golderman may have planned President Kennedy's assassination in order to have a spectacular piece of footage for a special TV program. Remember, Walter, TBC was a brand-new network in '63—buying the exclusive TV rights to the Zapruder film was our first coup. It built the network. So it looks like Golderman planned JFK's death to build ratings."

"My God," Krankit said.

I shared his concern. I've lived in this corporate gold-plated jungle long enough to care as much as the next guy about a forty-five share, but murdering a president was really stepping over the line. I decided that Golderman bore close watching. But right now, other things were on my mind. I picked up the phone and in a moment heard a delicious voice on the other end.

* * *

"Is that you, Kong?" Kathy giggled, using her pet pillow-talk nickname for me. Kathy was a curator for the Museum of the American Indian. She had round, firm breasts and a gorgeous ass, and she also loved Truffaut and Fellini, funny little Italian restaurants, and long walks in the rain. She was a real gem in my rhinestone and tinsel world.

"It sure is, honeypie," I answered. "Let's drive through the New England woods. Spring is coming."

Little did I know it was to be the last peaceful weekend I'd ever spend.

V

Kathy and I took my Jag up to New England and spent a weekend devouring caviar, lobster, champagne, strawberries, cheese, and each other. Whenever we went to a bucolic, pastoral retreat, Kathy's sexual tastes grew kinky. This time, she'd begged me to take my Sulka ties and bind her to the four-poster bed. Then, seeing the beseeching look in her eyes, I'd gotten out my suede Gucci belt and whipped her lovingly on her bountiful breasts and hard, round behind. "Ooohhh," she moaned as she writhed, "it's so easy for me to dominate every other man I know, but with you, Jack, I need to be tamed, ooooohhhhh!"

* * *

"Mmmmm, Jack, you're the *best*," Kathy said, snuggling under the downy quilt.

"Yeah, baby," I said, patting her cute little behind and jumping into my Hermes suede jacket, Meledandri cashmere pullover, and country flannel slacks. "But right now, I have a feeling something's up."

"It sure was last night," Kathy giggled.

"No, really." I looked out the window, where a thirty-foot black limousine with drawn curtains had been parked suspiciously all weekend.

Just then, Emily the innkeeper knocked on the door, summoning me to an urgent telephone call. I ran into the hall and picked up the phone. It was Angie, and her normally imperturbable voice sounded stricken.

"Jack, Jack," she sobbed. "It's Krankit—Walter Krankit, the news division president. He's—he's dead!"

VI

"But how—who—where?" I asked, back in my New York office after a frantic five-hour dash to TBC headquarters.

"It was an accident, Jack," Fred Golderman said, idly doodling "100" over and over again on a scratch pad. "He got dizzy and crashed through a floor-to-ceiling plate glass window in his office."

"Don't believe him, Jack," Angie hissed at me. "Krankit left this for you —said to only open it in the event of his death."

I hastily excused myself and went into my office, where I opened the envelope Angie had given me. When I read Krankit's note, I couldn't believe my eyes.

Jack (the note read): *I've just discovered that Golderman planned the 1973 oil embargo to force people to stay home and watch more TV. Still checking about deaths of Mao, Chou, and others. But the really horrible plot is about to begin. I can't write more—I think they're after me, no, no, arrrrrgggghhh...*

And the note trailed off. What, I wondered, was this monstrous plot of which Krankit wrote? I was still puzzling over this when Kathy burst into my office.

"Jack," she blurted. "It just came over the wire. There's been a terrible series of accidents at the other networks. ABC says that Henry Winkler, Cindy Williams, Farrah Fawcett-Majors, and the entire Osmond family have been wiped out in oddly coincidental accidents. CBS says a private plane just missed crashing into Mary Tyler Moore's company. And NBC says that Angie Dickinson and James Garner are missing."

I smashed my fist into the teak desk.

"*Golderman*," I hissed. "It was bad enough when he planned the killing of the president of the United States. It was bad enough he killed the Chinese Chairman, and shut off oil to the United States. But now he's gone too far—now he's killing off the *talent*. He's *got* to be stopped."

I noticed Kathy was reaching for me, loosening my belt and lowering my slacks. When she'd seen that determined look in my eye—the glint of a future network television president, fully competitive, yet not without commitment and idealism—she just couldn't control herself. She began to tongue me all over my cock, balls, ass, and thighs. And just before I yielded to the whirlpool of sensation, I thought to myself of all that I was risking in my struggle to stop whatever fiendish work Golderman and his allies were up to. Then it was over, as I came like a fountain all over Kathy's Ultima II lip gloss.

VII

The next few weeks proved my theory. Except for the writers, producers, and stars connected with TBC, the creative television community was awash in fear. James Komack was a living vegetable, the brilliance that had spawned "Welcome Back Kotter" snuffed out by the sneaking of lead-based paint into his luncheon yogurt. Norman Lear's studio was an armed camp, with tanks and machine guns protecting his company but chilling his creativity. And with the death of Krankit, Golderman had ordered the network news on TBC reduced to five minutes, so that he could put on a twenty-five minute cop show.

"My God," I said to myself late one night. "It's like *1984!* I've got to do something."

I'd heard that Fred Golderman was flying to the Coast for some highly secret meetings, so I booked myself on another airline that would arrive in L.A. at the same time. I tried to enjoy myself—the meal of foie gras, lobster bisque, rack of lamb, Caesar salad, brie, soufflé, and Chateau Margaux helped, and so did the three hours I spent in a lavatory with two comely stewardesses. They were amazingly limber; using the sink and toilet to brace themselves, they wound their long legs around their necks so that they presented whatever apertures to me I cared to use. And when we hit an air pocket, my strokes grew so powerful one of the ladies laughingly complained she could feel me "all the way up to my throat." But still, I was distracted.

I thought of the bloodshed, the cynicism, the money-grubbing that always found room for gore and violence, but canceled a "Young Porpoises" and other meaningful shows that could change the world. I thought about the sleazy sex and cheap, lurid pandering. And then I thought about Kathy and New England, and maybe getting out of this racket, teaching at Bennington, living in a quiet cabin in the woods. Who needed the Bentley, the Jaguar, the penthouse, the silk shirts, the boat, the private jet, the women, the Jacuzzis, the stock options, the dinners at Joe and Rose's or Chasen's or the Palm or Mike Manuche or Perino's or La Scala?

When we landed in L.A., I spotted Golderman heading for a car. I swiftly commandeered a Hertz Maserati and began to follow him. For hours we drove north, along hairpin turns, with tires squealing and brakes screeching. It was on the Maserati radio that I heard of the killing of Alistair Cooke, and the kidnapping of the entire cast of the "Carol Burnett Show," effectively stilling televison's finest satiric voice. The news only heightened my determination to stop this fiend.

Finally, Golderman's car stopped at the foot of a hidden driveway. I followed him as he pressed a secret button in a tree, revealing an incredible stone and glass mansion. I managed to sneak inside and followed Golderman as he entered a heavily guarded room. Using my judo and karate abilities, I silenced the guards and, with my heart in my mouth, opened the door to the secret room.

I couldn't believe my eyes.

VIII

There, seated around the gleaming, burnished heavy oak conference table, were the most powerful people in the world.

There was Shiekh Yameeni, wily Svengali to the oil-rich state of Aba Dabba.

There was Reverend Slung Yung Moon, sly mastermind of a fanatical religious cult whose dupes poured millions of dollars a day into the "minister's" mink-lined pockets.

There was Nelson Rickenfallow, former governor of a powerful Northeastern state, but more important, the most powerful member of the awesome Rickenfallow family, whose holdings in banks, oil, airlines, real estate, and fast food franchises totaled more than fifteen billion dollars.

There was Prince Bernard, aging prince consort of a cheese-loving lower European nation, who had been accepting millions of dollars in bribes from the world's most powerful corporations.

There was Katherine Grum, publisher of some of America's most powerful publications, seated next to Robert Midrock, the New Zealand press baron who had recently taken control of some important opinion-molding magazines. (I couldn't help noticing the swell of her breasts, and the look of frankly erotic interest in her eyes.)

All of them wore golden "100" lapel buttons, cuff links, tie clasps, or brooches. Hanging from one wall in the incredibly posh conference room were calendars, timetables, and a diamond-encrusted schedule for all four television networks. I noticed that the TBC schedule was radically different from what I had proposed: gone was the musical version of "The Young Porpoises"; gone was my groundbreaking sitcom about the Chicano and the crusty ex-army chef who owns a diner, "Spic and Span." Instead, there was just another lineup of cop shows, doctor shows, all with a violent, numbing sameness.

Then I looked to the head of the table; and I saw seated on a golden throne, the figure of...of...*Fred Golderman!*

"So it's...it's tr-true...." I gasped.

Golderman smiled viciously.

"Yes, Jack," he said, "And I congratulate you on your brilliance, courage, and indomitable will. You alone have penetrated the innermost recesses of our little—ahem—*consortium*."

"But who—how—why—what are you after?" I stammered.

Golderman rose from his throne, his eyes ablaze with horrifying fanaticism.

"What am I after?" he intoned. "The same dream I have pursued since my twisted, alienated youth, during which my only happiness was lying in front of my television set, having my mind twisted. The same dream I have pursued with absolute intensity every waking moment of my life.

"*A hundred rating!*" Golderman screamed, as the others around the table rose and screamed with him. "*A hundred rating! A hundred share!*"

Again and again, the horrible scream reverberated through the room.

"*A hundred rating!*
"*A hundred share!*
"*A hundred rating!*
"*A hundred share!*"

"Now you understand this symbol," Golderman said, pointing to his lapel pin and cuff links. "Now you understand why talent at every other network is dropping like flies. I will not rest until every television set in the world is tuned to TBC. Do you know, Jack," Golderman keened, "I have bribed the FCC to require a tiny device in every transmitter that will induce electroshock in any viewer who tries to change the channel off a TBC affiliate? In six months, we will turn the entire world into one vast TBC viewer! And nothing—no one and nothing—can stop us !!!"

I had heard enough. I wrenched myself free from the two bully-boys grabbing me and strode to the table.

"Listen, Golderman," I said quietly, and somehow the room was silent, and the world's rulers were listening to me. "You and your kind will never win. All you can do is kill me. But there are still thousands of Young Porpies out there; people of all races, creeds, income, and educational levels, who want something better than the mindless drivel you're feeding them. Go ahead—wipe me out; but there'll be others to take my place—to fight for diversity on network schedules—to temper profits with social responsibility!"

Golderman only smiled.

"Nice speech, Jack," he smirked. "Too bad it's your— *curtains* speech."

"Wait!" someone shouted. It was Katherine Grum. "I want to interrogate this man—*privately*. We publishers have ways of—*discouraging*—difficult creative minds." She motioned me into a small anteroom off the conference suite. Then, suddenly, she was on the floor tearing off her clothes.

"Oh, Jack, Jack, the minute I saw you I knew—I don't care about the conspiracy to rule the airwaves, I don't care about unparalleled wealth and power, I've got to have you—do it to me, Jack, oh, my God!" She was naked now, rubbing me with her slickly wet *mons veneris*.

"Sure, baby," I said, ripping off my clothes. I saw her eyes bulge as she looked at my crotch. "Just one little favor."

"Anything," she gasped, "anything!"

"Get me out of here after."

She stopped. "They'll kill me, torture me—but I don't care. Just give it to me—hard, harder, oooooohhhhh!"

She came three times in five minutes; then, she staggered to her feet and led me through an underground passage. I blew her a kiss, and ran down the path to my car. Before the guards knew what was happening, I was away. Free—but for how long? And where could I hide from this all-powerful conspiracy of the gilt-edged mind rapers?

EPILOGUE

So here I am, on the island of Penang. Golderman is right, of course; no one will believe this story. It's too crazy. But—but what if I pretend it's a novel? You know, disguise the names, change a few details, pretend it's all made up.

Can it work? Will the book clubs distribute enough copies to help alert the thoughtful, book-buying public to the menace of mindless television? Will the paperback houses commit themselves to enough publicity, promotion, and advertising to get the full, horrible story out? Will the few remaining independent movie companies help tell the tale so that millions more will know? And will those good forces enable me to obtain total financial security from even the most fiendish of Golderman's plans to silence all dissent?

On these questions, the future of mankind, and a great medium for entertainment and enlightenment, rest. Now I must finish this "story." For Kathy is calling: the sun is setting over our modest, but not inelegant villa; the cook, gardener, and maid are gone now. It's time for dinner, wine, and a night of sweet, sensual love to wash away the burdens of my struggle for a better world. I will fight again tomorrow.

The End??????????

THE REAL ADOLF HITLER

DRAKE TEUFELS

Over 438 weeks on the best seller list!

THE ONLY TRUE BIOGRAPHY
BASED ON NEW DOCUMENTARY EVIDENCE!

THE REAL ADOLF HITLER

by DRAKE TEUFELS

Adolf Hitler was born on April 20, 1889, in the village of Zwern, in Switzerland, near the German border. His father, Benjamin Hitler, was forty-eight at the time. Benjamin had worked in the local sausage factory all his life, starting in casings and wrappings and working his way up to assistant stuffing supervisor of the bauernwurst division. He fully expected to become head supervisor of this division when he was unexpectedly transferred to the outdoor drying department, a move that made him bitter and despondent. The outdoor section proved to be his undoing. A man with a delicate constitution, he was bitten by the Swiss dry fly, an insect that hovers around *Bunderfleisch*, Swiss dried beef, and caught a rare form of sleeping sickness in which only one eye closes. The villagers gave him a nickname, *Der Blinzelner* ("the winker"). He finally resorted to wearing a tinted monocle to cover the offending eye and regain some dignity in his appearance.

Adolf's mother, born Sigurd Pletzel, or "Ponzi," as she was called, was a lively, spirited woman whose smile showed a set of mischievous teeth, her best feature. Her son inherited the same bright, flashing teeth, which would have a mesmerizing effect on both men and women. Ponzi's father, Behrendt Pletzel, was famous in Zwern for carving miniature religious scenes out of chocolate.

Ponzi met her future husband while working as a spicer in the sausage plant. At that time, Benjamin Hitler cut a dashing figure, hoisting his pig bladders and stuffings in a swaggering, devil-may-care manner. The young lovers used to meet at the local café, where Benjamin spoke often of his dream to invent the perfect sausage, a wiener that would contain all the vitamins and minerals, all the nutritional elements man needed to maintain good health.

After they were married, Benjamin set up a laboratory in the basement of their little home on the Schweigerstrasse, where he worked every night on his miracle sausage, which he called *mannawurst*. His main problem was how to combine the nutritional ingredients with the spices needed to make the sausage taste good. "His mannawurst always tasted like spoiled fish and cabbage."[1]

Young Adolf grew up in a normal household, if we discount Benjamin's embittered behavior. Actually, the boy never met his father. Benjamin Hitler became a confirmed recluse, living in the basement and tinkering with his invention. He died one year, when a sausage containing dangerous chemicals blew up in his face. All Adolf knew about his father was what Ponzi told him—that he was working on a "secret project for the government...highly dangerous work with poison gases."[2] In a small provincial Swiss village, a boy believes and trusts his parents implicitly. To question parental authority was unthinkable, and Adolf accepted this explanation as a fact of life.

The only other surviving children in the Hitler family were the twin sisters Zoli and Yoli, who were ten years old when Adolf was born. He never saw them, either, because they had been sold to a family in Zurich at their birth. Twins were very scarce and highly prized in Europe during the nineteenth century, and it was common for wealthy families to make generous offers to the lower classes for a good, healthy set. The Hitlers received a substantial payment for their twins, but Benjamin squandered most of the money on his sausage research.

Hitler's early school records show that he was a hard-working but mediocre student. One of his teachers described him as "...almost always wrong in his answers...he would answer every question quickly and methodically, and entirely incorrectly. It got so I couldn't call on him no matter how eager he was to answer."[3] Although Hitler was poor in academics, which didn't interest him, he was brilliant in anything that caught his fancy. By the time he was nine, he was a walking encyclopedia on maritime law, chemical dyes, and vintage port.

Hitler's closest friend as a youth was Willy Frankenhosen, the son of the town barber. Willy was an enthusiastic amateur kidnapper, indulging in an activity that was not considered criminal in Zwern. He nabbed little children and held them for tiny ransoms, a few marks or even pfennigs. If the parents did not pay by sundown, he returned the child unharmed. It was like compulsory baby-sitting. Willy also taught young Adolf how to use makeup, a common custom for both young males and females in Switzerland. "He always wanted to use too much blush. He had such pale skin. He did not need so much blush. Blush was better on boys with darker complexions. The same with his eyeshadow. He always wanted to overdo it. Imagine dark shadows on pale skin."[4]

Hitler had a childhood sweetheart named Libi Straub, a tall, athletic girl who wore a full ski-type mask all the time, claiming she had been disfigured in a horrible accident and could not show her face. This was not true, but Libi wore it for dramatic effect, keeping it on for so many years that eventually, no one asked her about it or even cared. "Actually, Adolf always thought my face was made of wool."[5]

Libi liked to play a game with Adolf called "Laying the Egg." She would hide fresh eggs on her living room carpet, blindfold Hitler, and make him squat on the carpet in a laying position. The object of the game was to do a dozen "layings" without crushing any of the eggs. For years afterward, long after he and Libi had parted, Hitler continued to play this game. He could do a passable imitation of a chicken, and loved to show off how delicately he could sit on a raw egg.

While in his twenties, Hitler tried various jobs, but nothing interested him until he became a door-to-door salesman for the Adler Philosophik Company. Johannes Adler, the founder of the company, was a true believer in philosophy as the way to save the world. He taught his salesmen how to explain the basic ideas of all the great philosophers, from Aristotle to Hegel. After their training, his men would canvass a neighborhood much like today's vacuum cleaner salesmen do, except they would try to sell a family on a Kant, a Descartes, or an Aquinas. Adler was an idealist, not a businessman. His idea was simply to sell people on a set of philosophic principles that fitted their needs. If the family agreed with the salesman's pitch, they were given pamphlets, books, even complete leather-bound works. It was all free. The salesmen worked on a straight salary plus commission.

Hitler enjoyed his work and took great pains to dress the way he thought suitable for a teacher of philosophy, affecting an Oxford-Cambridge style—tweedy suits and odd jackets, baggy flannel trousers, or the traditional academic gown. He liked to clench an unlit pipe between his teeth, wear wire-rimmed spectacles, and adopt a professorial absent-minded-stooped-shoulder look. At twenty-five, he was well over six feet tall, slender, with a gaunt, ascetic face and blond hair.

One day, while on a door-to-door trip through the town of Knurl, about fifty miles from Zwern,

Hitler fell in love. It was a typical traveling salesman scene. Hitler tried to "get his foot in the door" and sell the prospect on Kant's *Critique of Pure Reason*, and kept getting the door slammed in his face. But he had an ingenuous, almost lovable persistence, similar to that of the young Jimmy Stewart or Henry Fonda. Finally, in desperation, he sang the entire *Critique of Pure Reason* under the customer's window as a serenade, making up a strange sing-along tune. Hitler's *sprechstimme* had a haunting, catchy rhythm that appealed to this customer, and she invited him in. He spent hours explaining the philosophy of Kant, but she didn't understand a word of it. All she wanted him to do was sing the words. They courted in this manner for three years, and were married shortly after World War I.

Hitler's young wife, Klaus "Kitzi" Spittsbard, was a transvestite, but was so feminine that it didn't matter. She was a stunning blond beauty with a lovely figure and perfect skin, in the best Germanic transvestite tradition. Hitler may not have even been aware that she was a transvestite. Evidently, Kitzi satisfied him sexually, and she in turn was attracted to his donnish, absent-minded professor look. Hitler settled down with her in Knurl and they seemed to be a happily married couple.[6]

Although Adolf had to be away on long sales trips, Kitzi did not mind. It wasn't until 1921 that she noticed that he was taking a bit longer than usual, sometimes as much as six months at a time. Hitler explained that his long absences were due to the new assignment he was given. He was now selling door-to-door in Germany, the birthplace of many great philosophers. It was a rich, rewarding territory, but needed a lot of work. Sometimes it took him months of discussion and arguing to make one sale. And on top of this, he was having a great deal of trouble pushing the work of the new "moderns"—Nietzsche, Hegel, Bertrand Russell. "Russell should be dropped from the line," he said. "Not only can I not give him away, I can't sing to his ideas. I could do better singing the words on the back of a cereal box."[7]

By a strange coincidence, a man with the same name was becoming a rising star of a new political movement in Germany called the National Socialist German Workers Party. He was about seven inches shorter than the Adolf Hitler of Zwern, his nose was larger and broader, and his hair was dark, while Hitler of Zwern's was light blond. The German Hitler also had a different physique—narrower in the shoulders, developing toward a paunch around the middle. He also sported a small brush moustache. Most important, his voice was entirely different. The Hitler who was then active in Munich politics had a deep, guttural but spellbinding voice, the voice of a born orator. The Hitler of Zwern had a thin, high-pitched voice, which was almost effeminate.

In one year, Adolf Hitler of Munich took over his party and became a fanatical nationalist, a brilliant propagandist, a skilled organizer, a wily political infighter, a vicious anti-Semite, and a man to be reckoned with in Germany's chaotic postwar period. From 1925 to 1929, this strong-willed firebrand worked to gain control of Germany. By 1934 he had accomplished this remarkable feat, and became the great dictator, the Fuehrer, the God-like leader of his country—a man with a ruthless, relentless drive to conquer the rest of Europe. What did this man have in common with Adolf Hitler of Zwern, the odd but harmless door-to-door philosophy salesman? The answer is: *they were one and the same man.*

Adolf Hitler, or the Fuehrer, as we shall now call him, was one of those phenomenons of history, a charismatic leader who simply happens to come along—a man with no antecedents, no roots—a man who appears in the right place at the right time, as miraculously as Joan of Arc or Napoleon. Where did he exist before he emerged in Munich? The best theory we have is that he was living in the mind, body, and soul of the other Adolf Hitler—the *real Hitler*, the Hitler of Zwern.

The process of emergence of a completely different and fully developed personality from the original is always difficult to explain. Today's doctors, students of ESP, and parapsychologists offer many theories, but, in this case, the basic fact appeared to be that "another life" existed inside Hitler of Zwern that demanded to be let out—a demonic and demented life, to be sure. We do know that the Fuehrer evolved fully from the Swiss Hitler, and in spite of lapses and reversions back to his "normal" identity, he became the dominant personality of the two.

Of course, after the Fuehrer came to power, he had the party historians invent a believable background for himself—a complete biography with parents, siblings, relatives, friends and so on. It was developed with typical German thoroughness. "Official" documents were created, pictures of the Fuehrer's "parents" were circulated, and an impressive war record was invented. It was a brilliant piece of work by Dr. Paul Josef Goebbels, the propaganda minister. But the fact remains that the Fuehrer was actually a split personality, a man with "two faces."

As we know from the many studies of the Fuehrer, he developed into an extremely emotional, unpredictable type, a man with mercurial changes of mood—intense changes that triggered a transformation of his identity. Many times, when the Fuehrer had a period of fear and self-doubt or weakness of the will, he would change back to his real self, Adolf Hitler of Zwern. Sometimes the transformation was so intense that it would last long enough for him to slip back to Zwern to see his beloved Kitzi. The Fuehrer's associates were astounded and mystified by his sudden changes into an absentminded, donnish professor over six feet tall with blond hair and blue eyes, who sang odd tunes to the words of the *Summa Theologica*. Most of the metamorphoses took place in private rather than in public appearances. The Fuehrer would retain his identity in large groups, but was susceptible to the transformation in the seclusion of his home or in small gatherings.

Dr. Goebbels, one of the Fuehrer's closest friends, recalled the first time he saw a transformation: "I remember the first time the Fuehrer went into one of his strange moods. I called it a mood, but it was much more than that. It was when he became another person. Or something like that. It was on February 27, 1933. The Fuehrer and I were having dinner at my home with my wife and children. He was then our chancellor, of course. After dinner he was in a very melancholy mood. He sighed and broke wind a lot and cried out that our task was too difficult—that our strong arm tactics were horrifying— that the Social Democrats, the Center Party, and especially the Communists were too much for us. I turned away for a moment to get him a small schnapps, a pick-me-up for his sorrowful spirits, and when I turned back he was gone—disappeared. Out of sight! In his place was a completely different person—much taller, thinner, and blond-haired. He was wearing a rumpled suit of tweed. The Fuehrer was allergic to tweed. It made him choke. 'Where is the Fuehrer?' I cried. 'Who are you and what have you done with the Fuehrer?' The man blinked, and looked at me as if I were a creature from another world, a Jew. 'Fuehrer? What is a Fuehrer?' he asked. I was about to call the Gestapo to arrest this oafish intruder when the phone rang. It was Putzi Hanfstaengel shouting that the Reichstag was on fire. I screamed incredulously. The Reichstag on fire? You must be joking! Then I turned back to the intruder and I couldn't believe my eyes. He was gone! In the second that I cried out that the Reichstag was on fire, the Fuehrer suddenly materialized as if nothing had happened. He screamed and shouted with glee. 'The Communists did it,' he said. 'Now we can arrest and execute them all!' I was so swept away by the news that I forgot about the strange transformation. Later I blamed it on the lingonberry brandy I was drinking that night."[8]

The incident in Goebbels's apartment was to be repeated many times. In moments of great stress, the Fuehrer would give an order, or make an important decision, and then suddenly transform: his mind would wander and his body would disappear, to be replaced by his true self. Over and over again this happened, from his earliest days as dictator of Nazi Germany. First the Fuehrer would decide to invade Austria. Then, a few moments later, having been transformed into Adolf Hitler of Zwern, the kindly don, he would feel deeply shocked and suffer great pangs of guilt and remorse. But almost always, it would be too late to rescind the order because of the incredible efficiency of the German war machine. Once a decision was put into action, the Germans blindly obeyed, even though they, too, were deeply shocked by the orders they had to carry out.

And so, this Jekyll-Hyde changed his identities constantly as he was drawn unwillingly into becoming the man of destiny for Germany. The rape of Austria was followed by the taking over of Czechoslovakia, the invasion of Poland, the conquest of Denmark and Norway, and the surrender of France. Each time the Fuehrer put one of his irrevocable orders in motion, he reverted back to his true self, and had the gravest feelings of doubt, melancholy, and remorse. The most horrible deed that he instigated and then immediately condemned was the extermination of the Jews. Again, the intricate apparatus of the Nazi regime was too responsive, too eager to carry out the orders of its tormented leader's evil half. Before he could say *nein, nein,* the Eichmann types were doing their jobs all too well.

New evidence recently released from German government archives indicates that some of the Fuehrer's closest aids, such as Goering, Himmler, Heydrich, and Bormann, could have been suffering from the same split personality syndrome, the same Jekyll-Hyde complex, *except that they had it in reverse.* When the Fuehrer issued his horrible orders, they would act shocked and dismayed. When the Fuehrer was transformed into his true self, they, in turn, were transformed into wild beasts, carrying out the horrible orders with frightening efficiency and fanatical zeal. The mind boggles and reels at the thought of what would have happened if the evil Hyde parts of these personalities were working together at the same time. The holocaust would have stretched around the globe.

Perhaps it would have been a different world if medical science had known how to treat Adolf Hitler's strange illness. Europe would have been spared, the phrase "concentration camp" would never have existed, and millions of people would still be alive today. We cannot theorize about such matters, but we can, in the light of today's knowledge of schizophrenia and psychosis, understand and diagnose the problem of Adolf Hitler. With this new insight into his plight, we can surely absolve him of direct blame for the crimes perpetrated by his regime. Indeed, no individual should be blamed. They were committed by men who were not fully aware of what they were doing, making truly human errors and then seeing them compounded by a massive, machine-like bureaucracy.

And what about Kitzi all these years? At first, she didn't mind her husband's long absences. He was a traveling salesman, and they were an essential part of the business. We must also remember that people were far more trusting in those days. Marriages were permanent and made in heaven, and love was eternal. And so Kitzi would busy herself with her hobbies while Adolf was supposedly cracking the highly receptive German market with his new line of philosophers. She liked to raise elephants, and would often ride one into the town square to do her shopping.

When Adolf did return home, he often acted strangely, as if he were atoning for some great sin. Kitzi would let him ride one of the smaller elephants, which would usually cheer him up. But in the late thirties, coinciding with the Fuehrer's rise to power, Adolf's visits to Kitzi became less frequent. Finally she could stand it no longer. She suspected foul play. One day in 1941, when Hitler wandered in, Kitzi began questioning him about his work, about his territories, and about which philosophers were selling well. Hitler was evasive and wouldn't answer her directly. Then she confronted him with an astounding fact she learned the day before. The Adler Philosophik Company had gone out of business in 1919. Hitler offered a lame excuse. He was selling on his own. Kitzi wanted to believe him, but couldn't. "And what are you doing with that odd dark-haired moustache?" she asked. This time Hitler had no answer. He looked in the mirror and sure enough, the familiar little moustache of the Fuehrer was still on his face. Somehow, in his transformation, the moustache hadn't disappeared. Hitler had no explanation. He left for Germany the same day.

This time Kitzi would not sit at home and wait for her husband. She decided to go to Germany and find him. When she arrived in Berlin, she was overwhelmed. All her life she had lived in a provincial mountain village in neutral Switzerland. She never read newspapers or listened to the radio, and so she had never heard of the Nazis and their overrunning of Europe.

She went to the most likely places to find her husband—public libraries, museums, tobacco shops, wine merchants. She said she was looking for her husband, a certain Adolf Hitler. The response to her queries was usually uncontrollable laughter, followed by mock seriousness, with directions on how to get to Berchtesgaden. Kitzi couldn't understand why people were laughing at her, but resolved to get to Berchtesgaden, if that was where her husband was.

Despite her naivete and inexperience, Kitzi had one great asset: she was a beautiful transvestite, and her particular type—tall, shapely, blond, with smooth skin and impeccable makeup—was the most prized sex object in Nazi Germany. Battle-hardened storm troopers, crusty old Prussian officers, vicious, scheming party functionaries—all these and many more wilted and trembled before this dazzling creature. And somehow, Kitzi managed to find her way into Berchtesgaden, Hitler's private

5

Adolf Hitler at age sixteen.   *Adolf Hitler, 1942.*

Kitzi Spittsbard, Adolf Hitler's wife, 1929.

Benjamin and "Ponzi" Hitler.

mountain lair.

The historic meeting of Kitzi and the Fuehrer was a great disappointment for one, a momentous occasion for the other. For Kitzi it was a terrible letdown. The little man she saw was not her husband. For the Fuehrer, it was love at first sight. He humored her about her nonexistent "husband," and promised to move heaven and earth to find him. Meanwhile he turned on all his charm and cajolery and persuaded Kitzi to stay at his luxurious villa while the search for "Adolf Hitler" continued.

At first, Kitzi was indifferent to the Fuehrer's lavish attention. But he made it difficult to resist. She soon became the court favorite—a spoiled child, a notorious flirt, and a highly skilled practitioner in the transvestite arts of sensuality. She learned ribald songs and performed mimicry and mime. The Fuehrer even had her elephants sent over.

When he was in a playful mood, the Fuehrer liked to keep Kitzi under the table during a meeting of the General Staff. In the middle of a complex explanation of military strategy he would instruct her to "wander about" and do her specialty on some of the more staid, dignified types, such as Admiral Doenitz or Field Marshall Jodl. Even Himmler was not immune to Kitzi's talents, and the Fuehrer loved to watch the stonefaced S.S. leader drool uncontrollably as his *pince-nez* invariably fell into his glass of mineral water.

Kitzi replaced the famous Eva Braun as the Fuehrer's mistress. Eva had been his secret companion for many years, stashed away in the villa, where she spent endless days reading cheap novels, watching trashy films, and hardening her fingernails. As Kitzi's fortunes rose, Eva Braun's fell. Eva was now totally ignored by the moody, impulsive dictator, and she was put in charge of catering office parties for minor functionaries. She despised Kitzi, and did everything she could to make her miserable at Berchtesgaden—frenching her bed, putting frogs in her vanity table drawers, and finally, trying to poison the elephants. Soon Eva and Kitzi had the Fuehrer's entourage divided into two warring camps, constantly squabbling and bickering.

Slowly but surely, Kitzi got the upper hand. By consorting with the Fuehrer and his staff, she absorbed a fair knowledge of military strategy and tactics, and was soon acting as a secret adviser to the group. Her under-the-table activities came to the surface, and the General Staff soon became her willing slaves.

Many of the German war decisions that failed were due to Kitzi's strange whims. She wanted to ride her elephants in the Russian snows, so she ordered the invasion of that vast, impenetrable country. She hated cowardice and ordered Rommel to stay in North Africa and fight to the finish. She hated France and did not want to hear intelligence reports about an impending Allied landing in Normandy. Eventually, she ran the war on the telephone from Berchtesgaden, and had all the food delivered from a delicatessen in a Bavarian village below. Eva Braun and her gang of wives and mistresses, the anti-Kitzi group, fled to a new set of quarters behind the mountain lair, took to patrolling their area with machine guns and rifles, and would kill a Kitzi supporter on the spot.

One day, when the Fuehrer happened to be in the form of Adolf Hitler of Zwern, he wandered away from Kitzi and stumbled into the hideaway of Eva Braun. Eva took one look at him and fell madly in love. He was a vision—a blond god, the true personification of Aryan beauty, though a bit rumpled and tweedy. The real Adolf Hitler responded warmly to Eva's unashamed advances. After all, the country was in a state of war and no one knew whether he would be alive or dead the next day. And it was the first time he had ever seen a real naked woman. Eva never knew he had a dual personality. Somehow, his transformations were kept secret. She thought he was a traveling philosophy salesman who was lost in the mountains.

In the spring of 1945, Kitzi decided that she wanted to go to Berlin to enjoy the operetta season and sit in the outdoor cafés. She was getting bored and frustrated in the secluded mountain lair of Berchtesgaden, and was also terribly anxious to do some clothes shopping. It took a lot of cajoling and temper tantrums and transvestite wiles to persuade the Fuehrer to go to Berlin at this time, because the Allies were getting dangerously close. But Kitzi finally had her way, and the entourage moved into the Fuehrer's town house.

Berlin was still a sin city, trying desperately to look the other way, even as the Allied bombs were devastating her from all sides. The Fuehrer was soon caught up in the city's dizzy social and sexual whirl, with the beauteous Kitzi at his side. One evening, after ingesting a strange drug from South America, he turned to Kitzi and asked about his old mistress, Eva Braun. He spoke of her with affection and even with undisguised lust, and asked Kitzi to arrange a double date, with Eva bringing a boyfriend. Kitzi could not dissuade him, and had to arrange a meeting with Eva, who was still lodged at Berchtesgaden. Eva agreed to the date and promised to bring her "new friend." When she arrived at the appointed hour alone, Kitzi inquired as to the whereabouts of the friend, taunting Eva, accusing her of not being pretty enough to have an escort. At this point, an eyewitness to the scene arrived, a certain Kurt Roemgart, who was delivering sandwiches and coffee to the Fuehrer.

"I walked into a big, comfortable room with many divans and soft pillows. Two women were arguing vehemently. The one called Eva, who was obviously the Fuehrer's old mistress, was saying that her boyfriend was late and would arrive soon. The other woman, who was called Kitzi, did not believe her, and said she was a lying, ugly hag. Eva then described her boyfriend's features and habits in the minutest detail, including many racy asides. Suddenly the Fuehrer, who seemed to be amused by the fight, was simply not there, and the man that Eva was describing appeared in his place. It was amazing. The Fuehrer was gone, and a big, tall man with blond hair was there instead. Eva cried in delight. This man was her boyfriend, her lover, her blond god. Kitzi cried out and ran to him as well, calling him her beloved husband. The man they both called Adolf was being torn and sexually ravaged by the two. I was both horrified and fascinated, hoping against hope that they would ask me to be the 'fourth for bridge,' as they say in Berlin. But they were too preoccupied. Meanwhile, I could hear the Allied bombs getting closer and closer, as well as the Russian cannons. I interrupted and warned them of the impending take-over of the city. I had to flee. But before I left, I witnessed a sexual act among the three parties that was so perverse and bizarre that I still cannot bring myself to write about it."[9]

Eva Braun, Kitzi Von Spittsbard, and Adolf Hitler were never seen again. Perhaps they escaped the Allied bombing. Perhaps they were killed, and their bodies never recovered. It would be fitting if this tormented man, this dual personality, was finally freed, and the two opposing parts of his body and soul were united, with the help of the warring Eva and Kitzi, in that final act of sexual perversity that we will never know about. God rest them all.

THE END

---

[1] Ponzi Hitler, *I Was Hitler's Mother*, Zurich, 1952.

[2] Ibid.

[3] Helga Schroeder, *I Was Hitler's Teacher*. Berlin, 1970.

[4] Willy Frankenhosen, *I Was Hitler's Best Friend*. Berne, 1955.

[5] Libi Straub, *I Was Hitler's Sweetheart*. Berne, 1965.

[6] "He would sing along to the works of Schopenhauer, David Hume, Kant, all kinds of philosophers, and his wife would dance a kind of hoochy-koochy, the way they do in America." Karl Wagenacht, *I Was Hitler's Next Door Neighbor in Knurl*. Hamburg, 1972.

[7] Karl Rippert, *Hitler's Adler Years*. Berlin, 1953.

[8] Josef Goebbels, *Complete Diaries*. Stuttgart, 1954.

[9] Kurt Roemgart, *I Was Hitler's Delivery Boy*. Hamburg, 1975.

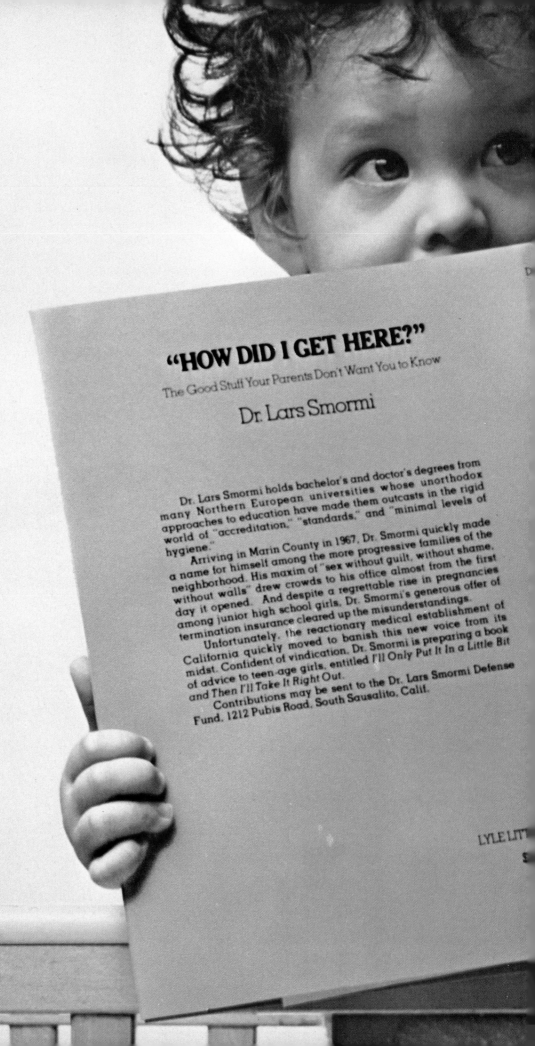

"HOW DID I GET HERE?"

The Good Stuff Your Parents Don't Want You to Know

Dr. Lars Smormi

Dr. Lars Smormi holds bachelor's and doctor's degrees from many Northern European universities whose unorthodox approaches to education have made them outcasts in the rigid world of "accreditation," "standards," and "minimal levels of hygiene."

Arriving in Marin County in 1967, Dr. Smormi quickly made a name for himself among the more progressive families of the neighborhood. His maxim of "sex without guilt, without shame, without walls" drew crowds to his office almost from the first day it opened. And despite a regrettable rise in pregnancies among junior high school girls, Dr. Smormi's generous offer of termination insurance cleared up the misunderstandings.

Unfortunately, the reactionary medical establishment of California quickly moved to banish this new voice from its midst. Confident of vindication, Dr. Smormi is preparing a book of advice to teen-age girls, entitled *I'll Only Put It In a Little Bit and Then I'll Take It Right Out.*

Contributions may be sent to the Dr. Lars Smormi Defense Fund, 1212 Pubis Road, South Sausalito, Calif.

LYLE LIT

S

"HOW DID I GET HERE?"
The Good Stuff Your Parents Don't Want You to Know
Dr. Lars Smormi
"HOW DID I GET HERE?"
LYLE LITTLE

We wrote this book because you've probably been hearing all sorts of crazy stories about exactly how you got to be here. We're not talking about busses or subways or cars or moving vans, but how you got to be born in the first place.

A lot of these stories make it all sound like a nasty secret; something you wouldn't want to talk to any grown-up about; something you'd want to hear with good friends in a place where you can listen and listen and rub yourself all over.

Well, that's fine, of course. But we thought we'd tell you *exactly* how it happens. That might make it even *more* exciting.

If you think *this* is exciting, wait 'til you hear the *whole* story!

This sperm is looking very hard for a very special friend.

Now, the only way you can make a baby is with a man and a woman. And the only way the man and the woman can make a baby is by putting their bodies as close together as they possibly can. They rub their bodies together and move up and down a lot and it feels like tickling and itching and swimming underwater and riding a pony and eating very cold ice cream.

It's called a lot of things: *getting your rocks off, making the beast with two backs, intercourse*. What it really is is *fucking*.

And when this happens, sticky white stuff called *semen* comes out of the man's *joystick* and wanders into the woman's *honeypot*. Inside the semen are millions of *sperm*, each one looking for a special *egg*.

2

Now, the egg and the sperm have to get together in a very special way to make a baby. They have to have a kind of very special arrangement with each other in a very special place called a *womb*.

When this arrangement takes place, the egg and the sperm get together and begin to grow together, inside the woman. When the woman finds out the sperm and egg are growing together, she is *pregnant*.

The sperm and the egg get together in the womb.

Lots of times you won't want to play the second half of this game.

Now that the egg and sperm have joined together, the tiny little speck just keeps on growing and growing and growing until it turns into a *baby*! Just like *you*! And when you get older—very, very soon, now—*you'll* be able to be part of this wonderful adventure. But just remember—some people find this wonderful adventure not so wonderful. Some people like to play the *beginning* of this neat game, but don't want anything to do with the rest of it.

If you would like to learn how to avoid most of this wonderful adventure, be sure and look for the sequel to this book, called: "AND I THOUGHT IT WAS JUST A BALLOON!" □

Other exciting best-sellers by Delores Lash

Passion's Thirsty Blaze
Lust's Consuming Fire
Love's Flaming Faggots
The Immolators
The Coagulators
The Incinerators
The Masticators
The Matriculators
The Enervators
The Perambulators

A DELVIKING BOOK

Love's Tormenting Itch

Delores Lash

I

"*Zut alors*, there's a tasty wench!"

Not again, thought Simone Battu as she marched haughtily down the dockside of Le Havre, her forthright bearing and powerful strides belying the sensuous flow of her legs and the sensual sway of her lusty thighs and hips as she bore her basket of wool caps atop her head of flaming hair, the color of a robust burgundy. Sometimes she regretted having blossomed so suddenly and abundantly into womanhood in the late French spring of 1815.

"*Eh bien*, I would sure love to put my *baton* in that sweet *rayon de miel!*"

Damn that crude, insensitive Henri Rudoyer, Simone thought, as she flashed her bright green eyes at the scene at the dockside of Le Havre. Merchants had wheeled their barrows through the broad and narrow street, hawking their wares as they lined up in ragged rows, beseeching passersby to purchase their goods. It was bizarre. Normally, Simone enjoyed the friendly give and take, the banter, the humorous exchange of kicks and punches that the young men of Le Havre enjoyed trading with the lusty young Simone. But there was something different about Henri Rudoyer. Perhaps it was the sinister, animallike gleam in his eyes that suggested he was undressing her in his mind. Perhaps it was the clammy feel of his hands as he attempted to undress her in his warehouse. Perhaps it was the barely concealed sadistic streak that lay beneath his bluff exterior; oh, Henri could be shrewd all right, but Simone had seen him holding one of his girl friends tight as he slammed her head against the wall of his store, and she knew that there was something wrong with Henri.

"*Mon dieu*, my little *morceau*," Henri shouted to Simone as he lounged against the entrance to his dockside provisions store, with its warehouse in the back. "You think you are too good for Henri just because my family is monarchist

1

while your father has risked all to serve that diseased monster Napoleon."

Even though Simone had promised herself to ignore the taunts of Henri, this slap in the face of her family's honor was too much. Simone wheeled to face her tormentor.

"You *cochon!*" she hissed. "Just you wait! When Napoleon smashes this putrescent Wellington, he will reign as undisputed ruler of Europe! Then the lands taken from my father when he was brutally murdered will be restored to my family, and the corrupt foundation on which your wealth was built will crumble like so much..."

Suddenly, a group of urchins rushed down the street waving freshly printed broadsides.

"*Supplementaire! Supplementaire!*" they shouted. "Read *tout le monde!* Wellington trounces Napoleon at Waterloo! Surrender seen inevitable! Louis XVIII to be restored to full monarchical powers! Everyone who supported the emperor's in bad trouble! *Supplementaire!*"

In a flash, Henri Rudoyer had leapt from his store, grabbed Simone, knocking her wool cap off her head, and pressed her roughly to his misshapen body.

"So, my little *montmorency*, where is that untamed haughtiness now! Your dreams are in ruins; *we* have triumphed! And now I shall claim my just reward!" He began to drag her back across the street to his establishment, urging her along by beating her across the shoulders with a barrel stave.

"Never! Never!" Simone screamed. "You *bête!* Rather than submit to you I would first rather be beaten to a bloody pulp!"

"That can be arranged," laughed Henri as he gathered the sinuously wriggling Simone into his hirsute arms. "But first, I shall have my way with you, brutally, painfully, and..."

"Not so fast, you common scum!"

The voice echoed resonantly, masterfully. Simone and Henri looked up. It came from a five-masted schooner docked at the most prestigious pier in Le Havre, the *Pier Hier*. The voice came from an imposing figure standing at the prow of the schooner, gazing down at the scene with a mixture of amusement and scorn. He was tall, towering some six and a half feet, with dark brown curly hair, piercing brown eyes, a craggy face, an aquiline nose, a cleft chin. Beneath the obviously expensive white silk shirt rippled muscles toned to steel; under the brown velvet pants rippled firm thighs and legs. A moustache gave his demeanor a mixture of dash and mystery.

2

Henri gazed up at the imposing figure with a mixture of fear and hatred.

"Who dares to speak to a loyal toady of his majesty?" Henri said, trying to thunder but only succeeding in giving off a squeak.

From the prow of the ship came a hearty laugh, a mixture of joy and contempt.

"I," said the man whose visage made Simone quiver with a feeling she had never felt before, "am Lord Faversham of Bedonshire—but it is just barely possible that you know me as—Captain Blacksnake!"

From the length and breadth—such as it was—of the narrow dockside street came gasps that were a mixture of fear and admiration. *Captain Blacksnake!* The daring buccaneer whose deeds were legend from the Straits of Magellan to the Isles of Langerhans! *Captain Blacksnake!* The privateer who had once been the most gallant and brave of the Royal Navy's officers, but who, after being cheated of his rightful commission, had broken with the navy to become the most bold and brave of the privateers that plied the seas! *Captain Blacksnake*—who had seized the treasures of dozens of the wealthiest families of Europe, and whose prowess with the most beautiful and haughty of women was legendary. "The greatest swordsman *and* the greatest swordsman in the world," was a common quip from Port-au-Prince to the Bay of Fundy. *Captain Blacksnake!*

"W-what do you want here? Stop interfering or...or..."

Before Henri could finish his thought, Captain Blacksnake grabbed a rope from the ship's rigging, swung down from the deck, seized the astonished Simone in his muscular left arm, and swung her back up to the prow of his vessel.

"*Sacre bleu*," bellowed Henri, "I'll see you hang for this!"

Captain Blacksnake put his fists on his hips, threw back his leonine head, and laughed. The sound made Simone quiver in a new yet oddly exciting way.

"You and what army?" quipped the witty captain. Then, turning to his crew, which had gathered on the deck, he bellowed out his commands.

"Full sail to the wind, my boys, and jibben off the fo'c'sle, for I smell the hint of treasure, and we sail the main at noon!"

"Huzzah!" the crew shouted good-naturedly, and scurried off to ask each other what the captain meant.

Blacksnake turned to Simone, and his brown eyes glowed with desire.

"As for you, my lovely little savory, you go to my cabin and wash the stink of that animal off your fair white skin. I'll wager no man's touched you like that... or any other way," he grinned with frank interest.

Simone's temper flared and she stamped her feet.

3

"Sir," she said icily. "I cannot deny I am in your debt for saving me, but think not that you can talk to me that way."

Captain Blacksnake threw out an affectionate left jab that snapped Simone's head back.

"Now get you below, my pretty lassie...I'll tend to you in a moment."

As Simone tried to clear her head, she wondered what the captain had meant. Could it be...did he possibly...he wouldn't *dare*! She descended to the captain's compact but opulent room and flung herself down on the bed.

II

Suddenly, the door flew open. A dwarfish creature, bearded and covered with boils, waddled over to her reclining form.

"Me name's Matey," the odious figure said. "Per'aps you've heard seamen speak of me. I'm sure the captain wouldn't mind if I pleasured meself on your fair body." With that, the slight but curiously strong figure began to pummel Simone with his fists and rip the clothing from her body.

Suddenly, the door flew open. Captain Blacksnake strode to the bed, picked up Matey, and hurled him out a porthole to the angry sea below.

"That's the last time I'll cancel liberty for the men," the captain said philosophically as he began to remove his clothing.

"What...what are you doing, monsieur?" inquired Simone.

"I'm going to teach you what it means to be a woman," Blacksnake said with a broad grin, as he gently but roughly stripped the dress from her body, leaving her clad in a camisole.

Simone's hands flew to her more intimate parts.

"No! No! You mustn't...." she said, but even as she spoke she felt a curious wave of desire sweeping over her body as Captain Blacksnake grabbed her left arm in a hammerlock, folded her into a half nelson—named after a great lord of the admiralty—and bared her magnificent body. Then he was on top of her.

"Please, please, mercy...mercy...merci!" she gasped. "You...you..."

"Damnit, woman," Blacksnake said in the throes of desire. "If you don't finish a sentence, I'll rip the tongue from your mouth!" And then he and she plunged into a vortex of love's consuming desire, fire's burgeoning passion, and for the first time in her life, Simone knew the essence of her tumultuous womanhood. Even as her mind raged at the indignity, her more developed organs knew this was her raging *raison d'être*.

Then Captain Blacksnake was done, and he lay back, sated, a mixture of satisfaction and exhaustion.

"So, my little minx, was this not what you wanted?" He was chuckling at her as she lay there, naked and bruised.

"I will never forgive you, you *chien*," Simone hissed at him. *No, no*, her loins protested, *he is everything you want*. But she continued.

"I will hunt you down to the ends of the earth to avenge this shame," she said. "You are my enemy for life!"

"Careful," the captain said, "for I've a sturdy stick with which to teach tempestuous hellions such as yourself some manners. Also a rubber truncheon, several dog whips, and a pair of brass knuckles…ah, but never mind that. For when we alight at New Orleans…"

"New Orleans?" Simone exclaimed.

"Yes, New Orleans!" replied the captain. "An old friend of mine, Jean Laffite, has helped a General Andrew Jackson rout the British, and as a reward, Jackson has promised safe haven for privateers. I suggest you enjoy yourself, my *petit dejeuner*, for we're bound for the New World!"

Oh, no, Simone thought. His words spun in her brain. *Bound. New world. He didn't look the type who liked to tie girls up, but you never could tell….*

III

The next six weeks were filled with adventure. Simone quickly grew accustomed to the daily routine: breakfast, midmorning rape, ship seizing, lunch, rest period, afternoon rape, clean up, free-play period, dinner, social, late-night rape; and apart from her regular visits to the infirmary, Simone found herself actually enjoying the voyage. Although she pretended to treat Captain Blacksnake's advances with indifference, she was afraid the captain knew how much she really enjoyed passion's raging lust—her screams of "*Mon Dieu, mon Dieu, jamais comme ci, jamais comme ça*" perhaps gave her away.

So it seemed like no time at all before one of the crew, seated high atop the mainmast in the crow's nest, waved his spyglass and shouted, "New Orleans! New Orleans!" And the crew gave the traditional response, firing celebratory shots from the fore deck freddie cannon.

"You may come ashore with us, Simone," Captain Blacksnake said indulgently, smacking her opulent rump affectionately with a broken piece of iron railing. "But see that you remain within sight or things will not go well for you."

Simone glared at him.

"I have no alternative but to follow your orders, you...you..."

"How can a woman who misses so many periods not be pregnant," Captain Blacksnake muttered.

And soon they were walking the streets of New Orleans! The fabled city, which Simone immediately loved for its adherence to the Napoleonic Code, was a wild frenzy of coffeehouses, taverns, wharves, Frenchmen, Americans, all decked out in colorful historical costumes.

"Come, Simone," said the captain. "I want you to come with me to a special place where only men such as myself and the lusty, brawling women they beat up are permitted." He led her down a crooked street into an unprepossessing building. But once inside, Simone could hardly believe it! She was in a huge room in which men in traditional pirate garb banged on tables and sang lusty, brawling songs, while women in low-cut dresses served tankards of rum, squealed as they were pinched, and frequently engaged in hair-pulling fights on the barroom floor as the men applauded.

Captain Blacksnake and Simone were given a special table, as befitted Blacksnake's reputation. After a few moments, a figure approached them.

"Excuse me, Cap'n, but..."

"Can it be?" the captain said. "It *is*—Oysters Bienville, the finest chef in New Orleans! What can I do for you?"

"Well, sir," Oysters said, "my employer wants to know if he might say hello to you."

"And who might that be—oh, by the Lord's sake, it's Jean Laffite!"

The swaggering pirate sidled up to Blacksnake and shook his hand heartily.

"Just wanted to say hello to the finest privateer in the world," Laffite said. "And who might this be?" he asked, pointing to Simone.

"A fine bit of fluff from Le Havre," Blacksnake said.

"May I?..." asked Laffite.

"Of course," said Blacksnake. Laffite threw Simone a left-right combination.

"Needs to keep her guard up," the pirate-patriot said. Then, turning somber, Laffite said, "Captain, I've not come for strictly social amenities. I've come to warn you. There's an enemy of yours from Le Havre who has attained great power in New Orleans, and he's sworn revenge on you. Name's Henri...Henri Rudoyer."

Simone gasped.

"Never heard of him," said Blacksnake.

"No, no, Captain," said Simone, "he's the one you rescued me from on the dockside."

Suddenly, the door flew open. Surrounded by twenty men armed with muskets, there stood...*Henri Rudoyer!*

"Seize him! Seize him!" Rudoyer bellowed. But in a flash, Captain Blacksnake and Jean Laffite had leapt over the table, drawn their swords, and run through eighteen of Rudoyer's lackeys. Then, seeing new reinforcements, the captain and Laffite headed for the door.

"I must flee!" Blacksnake said. "But Simone—remember—no matter how long it takes, I will find you. For...for...I love you!" Simone gasped as the captain fled. Then two of Rudoyer's running dogs seized Simone and began to cuff her.

"Enough!" ordered Rudoyer, who strode toward Simone, stroking his oleaginous cheeks.

"So," he said, "we meet again, my *grand mal*. Since last we met, I have received a charter from his majesty Louis XVIII for fifty thousand acres of land in Louisiana still held by his majesty's family. I have become worth millions of *reblochons* in gold. And I make you this offer. Stay here...be my mistress...run my estate...wear the finest of jewels and silk...or flee for your life through the fetid swamps of Louisiana."

"Now, let me think," said Simone.

IV

The next fifteen years passed quickly. Simone never got used to Henri's lovemaking habits—four rounds with the light gloves followed by fifteen seconds of immensely painful penetration—but the wealth and glamour were compensations. Still, each night as she lay in bed, wrists and ankles chained to the bedposts, she dreamed of the muscular, handsome Captain Blacksnake and the inferno's bubbling cauldron he had made of her inflamed fury's tissues.

Was he alive? Simone wondered. Was he still handsome? Had he perfected that right cross that had always given him trouble?

Then, suddenly, one day in 1830, the door flew open. Henri Rudoyer stormed in.

"We must leave immediately!" he said. "Terrible news. Charles X has fled France and the Duke of Orleans has been elected constitutional monarch! He has announced that all who served under Charles and abused their authority to make life miserable for their subjects while denying them the basic principles of elemental justice will have their lands forfeited. We must flee!"

"What do you mean 'we', Henri?" asked Simone.

Suddenly, the door flew open. There, looking every bit as handsome and dashing as he had fifteen years ago, stood...Captain Blacksnake!

Sweeping Simone into his arms and holding her so tightly to him that two of her ribs sustained hairline fractures, Captain Blacksnake swept Henri aside.

"Come, my *trompe l'oeil*, we must away. I am wanted by the naval forces of all lands, but we shall flee into Europe's interior, where I will once again teach you to be a *woman*!"

Simone's pleasure was as intense as pain.

The next three months passed quickly, as Simone and Captain Blacksnake, aided by Jean Laffite, sailed the treacherous Caribbean seas, past blockades set up to capture the notorious Blacksnake, and through the plains and mountains of Western Europe.

Finally, Captain Blacksnake paused at a beautiful mountain ridge to sodomize his beloved, and pointed toward a castle high in the clouds.

"But what...where...?" breathed Simone.

"Still with the mushmouth, eh?" said Captain Blacksnake. "Well, never mind. There's our new home."

"Where is it?" she asked.

"Austria," said Captain Blacksnake. "Where you will bear that son of mine you're carrying!"

Six months later, Simone was lying in her hospital bed, holding her brand-new son.

Captain Blacksnake entered the room, and kissed her without biting her shoulder as a special tribute to her delicate condition.

"A fine son," he said. "And in his honor, a special announcement. The Austrian government has given me a complete pardon and granted me a noble title, in recognition of my having created that splended Sacher torte for the duke. From now on, I'm to be known as Count von Sacher-Masoch."

Simone picked up the squalling infant. "You hear that, Leopold?" she asked, pulling at his ears. "From now on, your name is Leopold von Sacher-Masoch. And," she added, throwing him down and pounding on his bottom, "I'm going to teach you what being a little *man* is all about."

Memories of a waiter's thirty years at the Algonquin Round Table

CHECK, PLEASE!

WITH ORIGINAL SKETCHES BY THE AUTHOR, ELMER WINSLOW

VANITY FAIR PRESS

$4.86, service not included

Chapter One

IT WAS JUNE 28, 1914.
Eggs were six cents a dozen. Woodrow Wilson was president of the United States, Lillian Russell was knockin' 'em dead on the Rialto, and in a sleepy little corner of the world called Sarajevo, an archduke named Ferdinand was catching a headache that would soon have the whole world reaching for the aspirin jar.

But my own battle wasn't being waged in the trenches...and my uniform wasn't khaki green. Instead, I was attired in a short-sleeved white shirt, black bowtie, tan pants with a white apron. And I was standing in the kitchen of what was to be my "home away from home," as I liked to call it, for the next forty-five years— the dining room of the Algonquin Hotel!

Ever since my retirement in 1959, people have been asking me to write my memoirs about the years I spent watching and listening to some of the greatest literary people in America as they gathered around the tables at the Algonquin. My daughter Estelle, who never writes and hardly ever calls, will say, "Hey, Pop, why don't you find something to do instead of bothering me all day long— why don't you write a book about that place you worked?"

My downstairs neighbor, Tanoose the Communist, is always yelling at me, "For God's sake, turn down your radio with its stupid opiate music and do something useful...write down about the bourgeois artists whose mouths you helped stuff with the bread stolen from the workers!"

But I never did. I always believed that the relationship between a waiter and a customer was privileged...like with a lawyer, or a doctor, or a priest. What I heard, what I saw, stayed with me like the scrapings from a plate of goulash.

But then I got to thinking: what a shame it would be if the marvelous, inside, intimate glimpses I got of these immortals were to be lost forever to scholars and historians. The literary world has just about forgotten the people who once filled the dining room with laughter and tears. Sometimes two, three days go by without a book coming out about this wonderful group of folks.

So I decided: I'm not getting any younger, I have a pain in my shoulder you don't want to know about, and, as Jean-Paul Sartre once said over a plate of eggs—loosely scrambled, trim the crust on

1

whole wheat toast—"I'm not going to live forever." So here's a tray's-eye view of some of the most fascinating, quotable, and lovable collection of literary lions ever to beckon with a finger and a twinkle in the eye as they quipped: "Check, please."

So. Right. My first day. It was one of those nightmares. Everybody kept yelling for newspapers and running out of the dining room and screaming....I'll never forget that day as long as I live. We were stuck with at least a dozen orders of mutton, and Carl the maitre d' figures that World War I must have cost him $16 in tips— just the first day.

Chapter Two

A LOT OF PEOPLE HAVE asked me over the years, "Elmer, this Algonquin Club. When did it start?"

Luckily, I was there when it happened. It seems like yesterday....

One day in 1919, Marc Connally was seated all by himself at the big round table in the middle of the dining room. He was very well known at the time, publishing a very famous column in the *New York World* called "The Conning Tower." He never signed his real name; always the initials F.P.A. And I'll never forget this day, because every Wednesday, Marc—or F.P.A.—would order the Veal Holstein, an endive salad, and a schooner of dark beer. I would bring it to him, and every Wednesday he'd take a big bite, smile, and say, "You know, Elmer, this is *veal* good!" And we all had a good laugh over that one.

Anyway, this Wednesday, Marc ordered something different: it was an order of oysters with some shredded cabbage and a glass of white wine. As he was eating, two or three people came in. I remember one of them was the well-known playwright Franklin P. Adams. Jeez, you know, now that I think of it, maybe they called *him* F.P.A.! But that means maybe he wrote the column and Connally wrote the plays....

Well, who cares? The thing I'm trying to bring out is that there was no place for them to sit except at this big table where Connally was sitting all by himself. (Actually, maybe it was *Adams* who was sitting there, and *Connally* came in.) Adams—unless it was Connally—was very hungry and didn't want to wait, and as it meant an extra tip for me, I asked...whoever was sitting there if he minded if...the other guy and his friends joined them. Well, they really hit it off and Adams—I'm pretty sure now it was Adams who came in—really got a good laugh when Connally chewed one of his oysters and quipped, "Hey, Elmer, this is a *shell* of a good meal."

The next day, they were back and Dorothy Parker dropped in— and I mean dropped in. She was weaving back and forth and yelling something about "men don't make passes at women with empty glasses" or something, and she collapsed right in the chair next to Adams and Connally. Connally said something about not being able to make a silk purse out of a soused dear, and we all got a good laugh out of that one.

Pretty soon the word started getting around that you could have a good time if you got to sit at this big round table, and the next thing you knew, we had to put in one of those "Take-a-Number" racks, there were so many people waiting. I used to look at some of the younger writers waiting behind the rope we put up and quip, "You know, you're waiting more than *I* am."

Everybody got a good laugh out of that one.

Chapter Three

EVERYBODY USED TO SAY that if you were looking for a laugh, Robert Benchley was the guy you had to look for. I certainly remember how true that was.

I guess my first clue as to the really humorous character Bob Benchley was came in 1925. One Sunday we were setting up our buffet brunch, and all of the waiters were lined up behind the long table with the dishes stacked high and the chafing dishes steaming—we had a special German sausage we served with the eggs, which were flavored with chives and tarragon—and Benchley was just coming in from a late night on the town, in a tuxedo and cape.

Anyway, he came over to the table where I was helping set up the buffet, and he must have sensed that I didn't like working the buffet table. Not only didn't you get tips, but I always felt it was a step down from a real waiter's profession, where you carried a tray and everything like that.

So Bob came over to me, put his hand on my shoulder, and said, "Don't worry, Elmer—they also wait, who only stand and serve."

That was the kind of guy Bob Benchley was. Always good for a laugh.

Chapter Four

ONE OF THE BEST-KNOWN, and most-feared, members of the Algonquin Club was the late, great George S. Kaufman.

Kaufman was a very short, enormously fat man with a dapper moustache and a way of dressing that was extremely fastidious. He was a friend of almost every important person in the world, and was of course very well-known for his theater reviews, his radio show, and his book reviews—which could be enormously clever but kind of cruel sometimes.

It was always a matter of concern to Kaufman that he was so fat, and he was always trying to lose weight. I remember he ate nothing but lean meat all through the Depression.

In fact, Kaufman wrote a play about himself called *The Man Who Came to Dinner*, with Moss Hart, with whom he also wrote *Once in a Lifetime*. I even got tickets to that show. Funny, I always heard Kaufman was in that show, but the guy I saw was a tall, skinny guy with funny glasses and curly hair. Very Jewish-looking.

Kaufman's wit was famous, but those of us who hung around the Algonquin all the time—as waiters or diners—knew what most people didn't. Kaufman's lines weren't nearly as funny as his zany and hilarious practical jokes.

For instance, he would often stop by a novelty shop just off Fifth Avenue on Forty-fifth Street and pick up some truly wonderful items. He had this rubber doggy-doo that he would drop into a dish of beef stroganoff; he used to love to watch Harold Ross's face when the waiter uncovered the dish.

"Don't worry, Harold," Kaufman would say. "Every other part of the dog's in there, so what's the difference?" We all got a good laugh out of that one.

It was Kaufman, also, who put the whoopee cushion under Margaret Dumont's chair when that actress came by for lunch one time. I'm pretty sure that's when W.C. Fields got the idea to put her in all his movies and insult her.

Something like that.

Chapter Five

DOROTHY PARKER WAS one of the women who was always welcome at the Algonquin Club.

She was one of my most unforgettable customers. There were things about her you just couldn't forget. Like the parsley. Our chef liked to decorate the food with sprigs of parsley, but Dorothy Parker *hated* parsley, I mean *hated* it. So just about every day, she'd take the parsley off the plate and drop it into her handbag.

Well, this had been going on for about a year when one day she walked into the dining room with an enormous bouquet of parsley. She marched right into the kitchen, went up to the chef, handed him the bouquet, and said—softly, but clearly, "Here—I thought you'd like your parsley back."

Apart from her wit, Dorothy Parker—or Dotty, as she was known—was probably most famous for her drinking. She was, I have to say, the heaviest drinker I ever saw. She'd come in for lunch, put a quart of Scotch or bourbon on the table, and summon me over, calling out, "Elmer—I'll have a straw, please." Believe you me, that bottle was more often empty than not by the time lunch was over.

In fact, Dotty's drinking was responsible for one of the funniest exchanges ever spoken at the Club—and that would have to be some line, given the wits at that table.

Oh. Wait a minute. You know what I just realized? Isn't this ridiculous? That guy I told you about in Chapter Four? That was Woolcott—Alexander *Woolcott*. What happened was, I got my note pads with the drawings in it all mixed up. Sure, sure, Kaufman was the tall, skinny Jewish-looking guy I saw. Woolcott was the fat guy with the moustache. Wow, the tricks time plays on you.

Oh, right. So anyway, one time James Thurber bet Parker she couldn't go a meal without taking a drink. It was a pretty hefty bet in those days—$100, something like that.

"You're on," Parker says.

Well, everybody knew that Thurber was damn near blind as a bat. So what Dotty did was to slip me $20—which was a lot of money in those days—hand me the quart of Jim Beam, and tell me to pour it into a teapot. Then she called me over to the table and said, "Elmer, I'll have a nice pot of *tea*."

So all through the meal, Dotty's sipping her "tea" and getting happier and happier, chuckling at how she was going to win $100 off of Thurber, and Thurber is sitting there, getting more and more suspicious, because everybody knew Dotty couldn't go fifteen minutes without her whiskey.

Finally, he couldn't stand it anymore. He got up and tried to reach over to snatch the cup of "tea" Dotty was drinking. But he was so nearsighted, he knocked over all the plates and dishes and glasses—what a mess! Everybody fell silent, looking at the spills and the broken crockery, and in the midst of all the silence, Thurber looked around, smiled that little smile of his, and said, "Whoever called it near beer certainly had a poor sense of direction." Or something like that.

The Cooking of
Provincial
New Jersey

TIME/
ZUP
BOOKS

Welcome to the Cooking of Provincial New Jersey: Twenty-one Cuisines, One Great Taste

When we refer to New Jersey cuisine as provincial, we do not use the word to mean narrow, crude, or limited in scope. Quite the contrary, New Jersey offers a dazzling variety of dishes. We mean that the cooking traditions spring from the local foods sold in each province, or county, as they are called. For generations New Jersey cooks have managed to thrive on what they can buy from their native supermarkets, groceries, and "superettes."

Though each county owes its allegiance to the great state as a whole, the diversity in cooking styles makes you feel you are in twenty-one separate countries. When you are in Bergen County you will be enjoying a cuisine heavily influenced by the powdered foods and mixes, with frozen foods, food helpers, and canned foods equally as popular. Essex County, on the other hand, seems to like frozen foods, although it boasts of a strong following for powdered mixes, food helpers, and canned foods. In Monmouth County you can expect hearty dishes based on the local preferences for food helpers, but there are plenty of recipes that depend on frozen foods, powdered mixes, and canned foods as well. Passaic County seems to be equally divided in its choices among canned foods, food helpers, frozen foods, and powdered mixes.

New Jersey provincial cooking will always depend on time-honored traditions: on what the giant food processors are manufacturing, on the day-to-day shifts in supermarket inventory, and of course, on how much the food distributors are paying off the supermarket managers to promote or "push" certain foods, a widely-used merchandising technique that helps acquaint New Jerseyites with new palate-pleasing ideas.

Brooding gas tanks stand guard over a picnic spot near the town of Elizabeth in the county of Essex. Even at such an informal affair, New Jerseyites insist on traditional fare. Though it may take a bit of extra effort, the results are well worth it.

location photography by R. G. Harris

No one likes to miss New Jersey's Thursday Penny Saver Value Days because they know those pennies can add up.

The colorful, bustling New Jersey supermarkets: Fresh cartons from a nearby truck will soon be ready for sale.

New Jersey Kitchens: Meals in a Minute, for Any Mood

The perennial appeal of New Jersey cooking lies in its infinite variety and the effortless dexterity of the New Jersey cook in preparing as many as five or six completely different cuisines at the same meal. Dad, coming home from a hard day at the office, dreams of his Kraft Macaroni and Cheese casserole, daughter wants an old-fashioned Swanson turkey TV dinner, the two boys are waiting for their pizza and egg rolls to warm, and mom is treating herself to frozen Veal Parmigiana with spaghetti and Spatini sauce mix.

The fact that her family rarely eats together doesn't bother the New Jersey cook in the least. Her cupboard and freezer are amply stocked with delicious meals ready to be prepared at a moment's notice. New Jersey cooks do not go to cooking schools to learn their art. Tradition dictates that they learn the same way their girl friends did, in their own kitchens, where there are no professional chefs, no teachers to guide them. Each time they use a box of Roast 'n Boast or whip up a batch of French's Potato Pancake Mix, they depend solely on their inherent skills and excellent reading ability.

A canny New Jersey shopper examines a can of whipped topping to check its freshness, noting that it cannot be sold after July, 1989.

Every day, frozen fish sticks await the morning buyers in Hoboken, whose supermarkets are famous for their rich cargo of treasures from the deep.

The Prepared Food Mixes: From Powder to Perfection

The New Jersey housewife rarely uses a recipe unless it is foolproof. She knows that the prepared food mixes in her supermarket come from the laboratories of the finest food processors in the country. She's aware that every package of food mix she buys has been carefully researched and tested for ease of preparation, appetite appeal, and minimum spoilage probability.

Her cupboard of prepared food mixes reads like a *Who's Who* in gastronomy. She wouldn't think of using unknown "house" brands when she can buy the finest name brands at just a few pennies more, such as Lipton Cup-a-Soup, Hunt's Skillet Stroganoff, PDQ Instant Egg Nog Flavor Beads, and the hundreds of superb dishes from the Kraft and General Foods people.

This attitude reflects the kind of tradition we hope will never die in provincial New Jersey cooking—the respect for consistency and quality, and the trust in the good names of the food processors. New Jersey housewives settle for nothing less than perfection every time—because they know that if they follow package directions to the letter, the results will always be letter perfect.

A typical selection of powdered mixes bought from a supermarket in South Orange. The New Jersey cook can start her day with Tang and Maxwell House Instant Coffee, have some Betty Crocker Potato Buds for lunch, and build her dinner around Tempo Swedish Meatball Mix, Golden Grain Italian Style Risotto Seasoning (just add it to Minute Rice) and desserts like My-T-Fine chocolate almond flavor pudding.

studio photography by Jerry Friedman   Veronica Reilly, Stylist   preserve jar from Design Research   wooden bowl from Hubert des Forges

New Jersey's Frozen Foods: Modern Miracles of Freshness and Flavor

At the exact moment a snap bean or a succotash is ripe, it is carefully picked by the greats of the frozen food industry, such as Birds Eye or Green Giant. But the vegetables do not lie about. They go immediately to spotless plants, where they are flash-frozen at 200 degrees below zero to seal in all their flavor and freshness. Only then can they rest. First, in the vast frozen food section of a New Jersey supermarket. Then, in a New Jersey housewife's capacious freezer. But it is only a temporary sleep. For at any moment they can be awakened by a few measures of boiling water, and in a matter of minutes, a miracle has happened. Their original garden freshness has returned, and the robust appetites of a New Jersey family will be happily satisfied again.

A visit to the frozen food section of a New Jersey supermarket can span the continents in the variety it offers, from Holloway House stuffed peppers to Chun King Chow Mein to Jeno's Pizza. And for dessert, Sara Lee, Colonel Morton, Mrs. Smith, and a host of other master pastry makers tempt the discriminating shoppers with toothsome delights that make the finale of every meal an event in itself.

saucepan from Design Research

Boiling water is essential for preparing many frozen foods. A New Jersey cook has a trick for knowing when water comes to a boil. She will watch for bubbles to form. The bigger and more active the bubbles, the greater the boil.

4

Empty mix into shaker bag. Moisten chicken pieces with water or milk (about ¼ cup).

Shake off excess liquid.

Seasoned Mixes and Food Helpers: A Little Extra Work, a Lot Extra in Taste

Though Shake 'n Bake, Roast 'n Boast, and other seasoned coating mixes require extra work in preparation, New Jersey cooks gladly meet the challenge, because their tradition demands that they spend many loving minutes in the kitchen. And no matter how satisfied they were with their chicken, they are not afraid to admit that the great seasoned mixes make them even better.

Since New Jersey cooks have always added Rice-A-Roni and other instant starches to their meats and canned fish as "filler" material, the handy new food helpers were welcomed with gusto. Another good example of how provincial New Jersey cooking adjusts from the old to the new and creates a better dish in the bargain.

For the crowning touch, there's always room for plenty of salt, pepper, catsup, Kraft Miracle Whip, and mustard (the milder varieties) in a New Jersey dish. No matter how flavorful a dish already is, New Jerseyites can enhance it even further. Just a dash of this and a shake of that seems to make all the difference in the world.

lazy susan from Leonard Silver Mfg. Co. Inc.

Shake 2 or 3 pieces at a time in bag until evenly coated.

butcher block from The Door Store

Arrange chicken in a single layer in ungreased shallow baking pan. Bake at 400° for 40 to 50 minutes, or until tender. Coats 2½ pounds cut-up chicken.

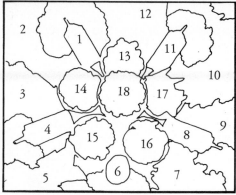

1. American Cheese-Flavored Aerosol
2. Pretzel Sticks
3. Potato Chips
4. Cheddar Flavored Aerosol
5. Corn Tacos
6. Bleu Cheese Flavored Aerosol
7. Barbecued Cheese Doodles
8. Meunster Flavored Aerosol
9. Pork Rind Flavored Chips
10. Cheese-It
11. Pimento Cheese Flavored Aerosol
12. Funyuns
13. Garlic Flavored Cheese Doodles
14. Beer Pretzels
15. Barbecued Tacos
16. Onion Taco Rings
17. Taco-Dippies
18. Hanky Pankies

The Snack:
Fast, Fun, Filling…Fantastic

No New Jerseyite would dream of a day without snacks. In fact, many New Jersey children devote their entire meals to snacks. New Jersey cooks put the snack to a bewildering variety of uses—as an hors d'oeuvre, a side dish to a main course, a main course, a dessert, a between meal treat, a TV "munch." Snacks are a must for picnics, car trips, for filling up fast and of course, to accompany the traditional New Jersey beverages, instant iced tea, Coca-Cola, Pepsi, 7-Up, and Kool-Aid.

Whether it is the simple potato chip, the Cheese Doodle scooping up a powdered onion soup dip, or the baroque swirls of Snack Mate American cheese aerosol spray on a Funyun, New Jersey is in love with snacks. And it's no wonder. For the snack represents the epitome of New Jersey gastronomy—it can be spicy or bland—it can tease the appetite or satisfy it completely. It is fast, yet fulfilling. The snack is the all-purpose wonder food that deservedly occupies the highest niche in provincial New Jersey cuisine.

The Hyman Kolnick Agency

Mr. Irving Hackman
Maison d'Or
Croesus Canyon Drive
Bel Air, California
"Irv!"
Dear Mr. Hackman:

    What can I say? What words are left? "Masterpiece"? "A classic"? You tell me, Irv. You're the writer. All I can say is, you've done it again. In all sincerity, I'm proud and humble to be associated with an artist in his own right. You have created another work that will both entertain and inform your legion of fans and admirers the world over.

    Now for some business details. I hesitate bothering a creative person such as yourself, but let me keep you informed so you can return to your work.

    The floor bid on the paperback is 500K; Dick says it'll more likely hit a million-two. It looks like film rights will be between a Universal limited series and a Columbia theatrical. Either way, the three-fifty thou is a rock bottom estimate, and on both you have the "creative consultant" tag for another 150K. Sylvia figures first serials leveling off somewhere in the hundred grand area; and it's too soon to get a hard count on foreign rights.

    On the tour: Sandy has set up thirty-five cities in forty-one days. We've double-checked the hotel suites (I'm sorry about the sauna on the last tour--believe me, Irv, it won't happen again), and there'll be TV in the limos everywhere.

    Sandy also says that the London-Paris-Geneva swing may be technically "tricky" since the book won't be out in Europe for nine months, but she's certain that Dick will understand your need for a research trip to plan your next opus. So don't worry.

    Irv, I couldn't be more pleased, and I hope you feel the same way. When you get to New York, we'll put on another "do." There's a certain receptionist over here who's <u>really</u> looking forward to "seeing" you again--hah-hah. Best to Bess.

Your fan and agent,

Hyman Kolnick

Irv—Don't sweat the audit. I think
everything's been "taken care of."

4002 East Fifty-Seventh Street
New York, N.Y. 10022
Cable: "Hikolonik"

The White House Is Sinking!

by

Irving Hackman

711 East Ninth Street
New York, N.Y.
July 8, 1979

Dear Mr. Hackman:

Here's the research. I hope it's okay, 'cause I spent three months on it and almost flunked out of school. I figure 300 hours at $2.75 an hour comes to $825, plus $65 in expenses.

I hate to bother you when you're so busy writing, but I could use some of the money real quick, 'cause of Mom.

Thank you.

Sincerely,

Sarah McRae

Sarah McRae

Marz - Buck This bitch to the publisher. It's research and I won't pay a dime of it.

Ivo.

THE WHITE HOUSE IS SINKING

Chapter One

The red telephone on President William Brown's desk rang
insistently.

"Uh, oh," President William Brown thought to himself as he
gazed out of the window of his White House Oval Office. "This
could mean trouble."

He felt a flash of doubt as the pressure of his job pressed
down on him. Should he have ever run for this office, campaigning
across fifty states, in an effort to win a majority of
electoral votes, which are calculated by adding the number of
representatives to the two senators that each state has under
the Constitution? The new treaty with Russia, the Domestic Progress
Corps--was it worth it?

President Brown sighed again and picked up the phone.

"Yes," he barked into the phone.

"This is McIntyre," said Secretary of State Bob McIntrye,
who headed the Department of State, the first cabinet department
ever established in the United States, in 1793, which was charged
with the job of carrying out American foreign policy, and whose
secretaries had included such important people as Daniel Webster,
William Jennings Bryan, Cordell Hull, John Foster Dulles, and Henry
Kissinger.

"Yes," said President Brown, glancing again out of his window,
and noticing that the flowers in the Rose Garden were growing unusually
tall this year, and that the trees seemed to tower taller than ever.
Curious....

"Mr. President," said McIntyre urgently, "I must see you
immediately. It's a matter of utmost national security."

"Can you tell me--"

"Not even on the red phone, sir," said the secretary.

"Very well," said the president, William Brown. "Come right over...no, wait," he added, remembering his next appointment with a flush of excitement. "Give me thirty minutes."

"Right," said Secretary McIntyre, hanging up the phone.

What new crisis could it be? William Brown, president of the United States, wondered. Then, feeling himself growing steadily more excited, he buzzed the intercom.

"Miss Thysson, please come in for a moment," he said, his voice husky.

"Certainly, sir," said a soft, sweet voice with a hint of a giggle. The president felt himself growing still more excited. He managed to push all thoughts of that urgent matter of Secretary McInty from his mind as he looked up at the sun, which was concealed by the White House foliage. Have to talk to the gardener about that, he thought.... Then there was a knock on the door. Cecilia Thysson!

Chapter Two

"You rang, Mr. President?" Cecilia said, sinuously pressing up against William Brown's body.

"No, it's you who always ring my chimes, Cecilia," William Brown said, as he ran his hands up and down her firm, sensuous hips and thighs. His voice grew husky as he urgently pulled the crimson sheath off her firm, white body. He gazed eagerly at her firm white breasts, her firm white belly, her hidden mystery of womanhood.

"I want you here--now--on the Wilson desk," the president said as he pressed her down, scattering several urgent briefing memos from the National Security Council, a top-secret

agency charged with the duty of assessing the United States's security
position vis-a-vis other nations of the world.

"Oooh, Mr. President," gasped Cecilia Thysson as she writhed
her firm white buttocks on the desk.

"Don't you know this _isn't_ the Wilson desk?" She nibbled
the president's ear and urged him further inside her.

"Wha-what?" gasped President William Brown in the throes of
carnal passion.

"No, no," Cecilia breathed heavily. "Most people believe
this desk was used by Woodrow Wilson, who served as president of the
United States from 1913 to 1921, after having been governor of
New Jersey and before that president of Princeton University. But
in fact--ooh, do that some _more_--it wasn't used by Woodrow Wilson. It
was used by Henry Wilson, who served as vice-president under Ulysses S.
Grant, who served as president from 1869 to 1877, after having led
the Union Army to a successful victory over the Confederates during
the Civil War, which divided the United States from 1861 to 1865.

"Oh my God, oh my God," gasped the president.

"Don't worry, darling," moaned Cecilia. "Nobody will know."

"Oh my God!" the president screamed, as his body shuddered with
release. "I think I felt the earth move!"

"Me, too," Cecilia sighed. "Like we were..._sinking_ or something."

Suddenly, the door flew open.

"Mr. President!"

Turning their heads, William Brown and Cecilia Thysson gazed
into the stern countenance of Secretary of State Bob McIntyre!

Chapter Three

"Bob!" the president exclaimed. "What--who--?"

Dear Mr. Hack

Here's th
I spent three
of school. I i
to $825, plus $

I hate to
writing, but I c
quick, 'cause of
Thank you.

Marz - Bu

It's resea

dime o

"I told your secretary this was a matter of urgent national security. When she told me something big had come up in your office, I had no idea...."

McIntyre gazed with wintry disapproval at the half-clothed body of President William Brown and the firm, white naked form of Cecilia Thysson.

"Miss Thysson," the secretary of state said, "please leave immediately."

"Y--yes, sir," Cecilia said, grabbing her dress in a futile attempt to conceal her lush figure.

"Bob," the president said, resuming his seat behind the desk that had not been used by President Woodrow Wilson, "what's the meaning of this intrusion?"

"I told you over the phone, Mr. President, that this was a matter of the most urgent national security. Mr. President, come over here by the window--and tell me if you notice anything different about the foliage."

The president strode over to the window and looked out at the lovely landscape, one of the most beautiful in all the nation's capital.

"Why--it seems as if the trees and flowers are getting taller."

"Yes, Mr. President," the secretary of state said grimly. "That's what is seems like. But," he went on, in a tone fraught with danger and foreboding, "the truth is something different--something that, if it ever became public, would jeopardize the very existence of the United States of America!"

The secretary paused for a moment, then plunged on.

"Mr. President," Bob McIntyre said in a quavering voice, "Mr. President: the White House is sinking!"

Chapter Four

"What?" exclaimed President William Brown. "I don't understand!"

"I know it seems incredible, Mr. President," Secretary McIntyre
said. "That's why I've asked someone here who could explain this
incredible situation." The secretary walked to the intercom and
pressed down the buzzer.

"Would you send Mr. Antonelli in, please?"

"A moment later, a short, middle-aged man with gray hair and
a rumpled corduroy suit walked into the Oval Office.

"Mr. President." said Bob McIntyre, "this is Tony Antonelli:
chief engineer of the National Parks Service. The White House
is under the jurisdiction of the National Parks Service;
so Mr. Antonelli can fill you in."

The chief engineer dug into his battered briefcase and pulled
out an enormous sheaf of paper.

"Mr. President," Antonelli began nervously, stuffing a pipe
and lighting it as he juggled the papers, "I've had some research
done on this problem, and I think it will give you some idea of
what's going on."

"Fine," said Secretary McIntyre impatiently. "Just remember--
this is absolutely top secret."

"Right, right," Antonelli nodded. He shuffled through his papers
and relit his pipe.

"As you know, Mr. President, Washington--or the District of
Columbia, as it's formally known--is an area of some sixty-eight square
miles that was carved out of the state of Maryland in 1788. It's
been a municipal corporation since 1871; at first, it was some
30.75 square miles bigger, but that land was returned to Virginia
in 1846."

Antonelli puffed on his pipe as the president and the secretary
of state listened intently.

Antonelli continued. "It was the first carefully planned capital in the world, designed and originally laid out by Pierre Charles l'Enfant, and completed by Major Andrew Ellicott."

Antonelli took the pipe out of his mouth and gestured for emphasis.

"The White House," Antonelli continued, "is an important part of this plan. It was first built in 1792 following a design by James Hoban, an Irish-born architect. There were many delays in its construction, but it was completed--almost--in 1800, and John Adams moved in. Under Jefferson, himself an amateur architect, the east and west pavilions were built. In 1814, when the British burned the White House, a coat of white paint was used to cover the damage--hence the term "White House," at least in myth. Actually, the name was employed from the building's beginnings."

"Yes, yes," said President William Brown impatiently, "but what has all this to do with--"

"I'm coming to that, sir," Antonelli said, relighting his pipe.

"As you must realize, throughout the years, the White House has undergone extensive improvements. Gas lighting was introduced in 1848; central heating in 1853; the first bathroom was installed in 1877; in 1902, the house was extensively restored, and in 1949, a ste and concrete frame was placed in the White House, around which the original design was rebuilt. At that time, President Truman moved into Blair House.

"Now," said Antonelli, puffing again on his pipe, "apparently, from the very beginning, the White House was somehow located on a hidden marsh. Because the original design was of wood and plaster, it didn't really matter. But over the years, as more and more heavy underpinning and additions were placed on the building, the entire edifice has begun to sink--slowly at first, then faster and faster.

"Mr. President," Antonelli said, "we estimate that the White Hous is sinking at the rate of six inches a month." He placed the papers back in his briefcase and puffed on his pipe.

Dear Mr. Hack

Here's th
I spent three
of school. I
to $825, plus $
I hate to
writing, but I
quick, 'cause of
Thank you.

Marz - Bu

H's resea

dime

"Will you put that goddamned pipe away," President William Brown
said, coughing through the cloud of smoke that pervaded the Oval Office.
"Bob," the president said, "I just don't see what the issue is. If
the White House is sinking, let's just fix it."

"I'm afraid it isn't that simple, sir," Secretary McIntyre said.
"We've got that treaty coming up with the Soviet Union, a nation of
more than 250 million under a bureaucratic Communist regime that was
established in October, 1917. They have an instinct for weakness; if they
see any sign of vulnerability on our part, they're likely to undo
the entire treaty. It could mean World War III."

"My God," the president said. "It's unbelievable!"

"Unbelievable--but true," the secretary replied. "That's why
we need another plan--and that's why I've asked Smithfield Porcine,
director of the Central Intelligence Agency, to come over here and
brief you on a plan we've worked out."

"What kind of plan?" the president asked.

"Well, sir," said the secretary, "it's offbeat--almost bizarre.
But it's so crazy, it just might work. He should be here any--"

BA-ROOOOOOOOOOOOOOOOOOOOOM!!!!!!!

A huge explosion shattered the calm! A fiery ball of orange
flame lit up the sky!

Gunshots echoed through the air!

Tires and brakes screeched!

Voices screamed!

Three men from the Secret Service, an agency under the Department
of the Treasury, created in 1865 and charged with protecting presidents
after the 1901 assassination of William McKinley, ran into the Oval
Office and leapt on top of the president.

Suddenly, all was still.

Bob McIntyre crawled over to the window and looked out.

"My God!" he shouted. "It's Smithfield Porcine's car! It's all
blown up! Blood and guts are everywhere! He's dead!"

Chapter Five

The president looked around the wooden oak table. The faces were somber, grave. Secretary McIntyre, F.B.I. Director Grant Strong, National Security Adviser Zvigibrinx Krbrinski, Parks Engineer Antonel

"All right," the president said. "What happened?"

"Dynamite," said Strong, "the explosive device invented by Alfred Nobel in—"

"Please," said the president. "Not now. But who--why?"

"Because, Mr. President, somebody doesn't want our plan to succeed," Strong said. "Somebody wants the White House to keep sinking. In other words," Strong said, "somebody is a traitor. Somebody...in this room!"

A shocked silence was heard.

Chapter Six

"But who--why?"

President William Brown paced back and forth in the Lincoln bedroom

"We don't know, sir," said McIntyre, who, along with Strong, had been summoned by William Brown out of the formal meeting and up to the bedroom on the second floor of the White House. "All we know is that somebody wants you to appear weak, foolish, and indecisive in the eyes of the world, threatening the entire existence of our Republic: a form of government in which the chief of government, fused with the role of chief of state, is elected directly by the people."

"Wait a minute," the president said. "Why must we worry so much about this White House sinking? Why can't we just announce we're making renovations--move me somewhere like Blair House?"

"It's not that simple, sir," McIntyre said. "You see, according

to the law, you would be unable to leave the White House for an
extended period of time without consulting the Federal Transportation
Administration. In addition, no work can be done to restore the
White House before filing an environmental impact statement
with the EPA, as well as very detailed health and safety proposals
with the Occupational Safety and Health Administration. Furthermore,
all prospective employees must meet careful regulations designed to
promote racial, sexual, lifestyle, gender, and orifice preferences
according to the latest amendments to the Civil Rights Act."

"I see," said the president, in a short paragraph.

"So," said McIntyre, "you really have no choice but to remain
here, inside the White House, until it sinks beneath the surface,
killing you and everyone inside it. Unless, of course, we can put
into effect the plan that CIA Director Porcine was coming here to
report to you before he was blown up by the traitor who was here,
inside the White House."

"Have you any idea who this traitor is?"

"Yes, Mr. President," said Strong. "The name of the traitor, the
name of this Benedict Arnold--a highly regarded Revolutionary War
general who betrayed his cause for British gold--is--arrrrgggg!"

Strong gasped!

He clutched his heart!

He fell dead!

"Good Lord," the president said. "He's dead!"

"Just as I suspected," said McIntyre. "This proves it!" He
raced to the door of the room and shouted at the Secret Service.

"Bring in the prisoner!"

A moment later, two burly men entered the room, dragging with them
the twisting, wriggling, sinuous form of--Cecilia Thysson!

Chapter Seven

"You?!" the president gasped.

"Yes, Mr. President," said Secretary McIntyre. "She was attempt
to distract you with her obvious charms from even noticing that the
White House was sinking. We have reason to believe she is in the pay
of the Cubans--or Russians--or French--or whoever wants to weaken
this country."

"No, no," the sinuous, white, firm redhead cried. "It's not
true--I love you, Mr. President. I love the way your body feels
when the penis, made erect by the sudden flow of blood into the organ
stiffens the erectile tissue and makes it ready to enter the lubricat
orifice. I do. I do."

"Don't listen to her," said the suddenly nervous secretary of sta
"It's nothing but--"

Suddenly, the door flew open. In ran a dozen youths, wearing
the uniform of the Domestic Progress Council. One of them brandished
a laser gun.

"Mr. Secretary," said Cecilia Thysson, wriggling sensuously free
of the Secret Service grasp. "In the name of the Domestic Progress
Corps, I arrest you for high treason...for plotting to overthrow the
president of the United States."

"Prove it," snarled the suddenly villainous Cabinet member.

"We will," Cecilia said. She turned to the president and,
unclasping her handbag, pulled out a sheaf of papers.

"You see, Mr. President," Cecilia said, "under the Act of
Succession, codified by the Twenty-sixth Amendment, proposed by the
Congress in 1947 and ratified by the states in 1951, if the president,
vice-president, Speaker of the House, and president pro tempore of the
Senate are all disabled from assuming the presidency, the secretary
of state becomes president.

Dear Mr. Hackm

Here's the
I spent three m
of school. I fi
to $825, plus $6
I hate to b
writing, but I co
quick, 'cause of
Thank you.

"What McIntyre did," Cecilia continued, "--you don't happen to have a cigarette or a pencil, or something to fidget with, do you-- anyway, McIntyre bribed Antonelli to dig out the foundations of the White House. His plan was to trap you, the vice-president, the Speaker--"

"For God's sake," President William Brown said.

"...to trap all of you in the White House as it was sinking, and assume the presidency for himself."

"And to think I almost fell for it," the president said. "Take him away, boys." The Secret Service hustled the secretary off to await trial, which under the criminal code of the United States,
                    (MARG: INSERT TITLE XIX HERE)

"And now," said President William Brown, as he drew the sinuous white body of Cecilia Thysson to him, "how did you discover the plot?"

"Well," Cecilia said, "I was assigned by the Domestic Progress Corps as a White House intern. After you and I--you know," she giggled, "I began suspecting McIntyre. Call it women's intuition. So we've been watching him carefully...it was only today we figured it out. He blew up Porcine; he poisoned Strong. And if we hadn't stopped him--"

"I know," said President William Brown as he pressed her onto the bed of the bedroom. "We wouldn't be able to do <u>this</u>." He ripped the clothes off her body and began to hold her urgently....

                    THE END

THE BOOK OF FINGS

If you liked The Book of Fings, here are some other Over-Price Non-Books you'll probably like, too:

Aren't Puppies Nice?
I Love You So Much I Could Shit!
Aren't Kittens Cute?
Cooking Without Food
This Is Just to Say I'm Pleased to Meet You!
I'm Sorry About Last Night, Honey

THE BOOK
OF
FINGS

$6.95
An Over-Price Non-Book

Some Fings are LITTLE...

Some Fings are BIG!

Some Fings are NAUGHTY...

Some Fings are NICE!

Some Fings are HARD TO SEE...

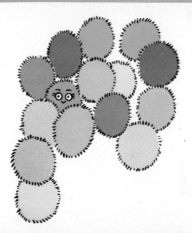

You have to look TWICE!

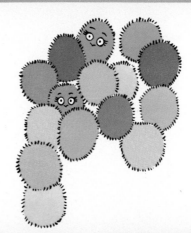

Sometimes, Fings aren't what they seem.

"Just one of those Fings" again....

Sometimes it's great to "do your Fing…"

Or go Fingin' in the rain!

And sometimes Fings are tough all over, but…

Most of the time, Fings are looking up!

Dr. Mildred Sternfricker has long been hailed as one of the world's great pioneers in therapy. She has said that as long ago as college, she realized "the musty volumes of Freud, Jung, and Adler, with their needlessly complicated verbiage and small type, with no pictures or anything" were barriers to effective treatment of anxiety and stress in the modern world rather than guideposts.

Starting with a small, select clientele, Dr. Sternfricker quickly gained the esteem that is so rightfully hers: from the maitre d' at Ma Maison to the parking lot attendant at La Scalla, the West Coast community recognizes in Dr. Sternfricker the level of achievement that merits the very special recognition of her peers.

Willie Cashin is a free-lance writer whose work has appeared in *Family Today*, *Men's Action*, and *Spurt* Magazine.

For $50 an Hour,
I'll Be Your Own
Best Friend
(Plus, You Get Lunch)

How to
Get More
Out of Everybody

Dr. Mildred Sternfricker

with
Willie Cashin

"Before I discovered Dr. Sternfricker, I was writing for the *Soho News* at $75 a shot. Thanks to this marvelous woman, I've signed a three-picture deal with Warner's for a big six up front and points up the old wazoo. She has changed my life."

—Penelope Giddyup

"I would not go anywhere without this book. Hey, I'm not kidding. I won't get out of bed without this book. (I also won't get out of bed for less than $50K, and I'm talking postcards.) I won't go to the kitchen, I won't go to the bathroom, I won't leave the house, I won't open my eyes and wake up unless I'm holding this marvelous work, which has liberated me from my fears and hang-ups."

—Erica "Ma" Jongg

"I mean, depression…I mean, who *needs* it? It makes you frown, and get, you know, wrinkles, and you bite your nails, and I mean, nails with bites are, I mean, a *disaster.…*"

—Marisa Berenson

"Remarkable…sure to be a best seller…can't miss…astonishing…there is no limit…the…public…will buy (it)….

—*The New York Times*

"Thank you for sending us a copy of this book. In accordance with provisions of registered mail, we acknowledge receipt."

—American Psychological Association

INTRODUCTION

I first became aware of the remarkable Dr. Sternfricker two years ago, when I was working as an associate reporter for "Rona Barrett's Hollywood." My job was to attend important parties in Hollywood in order to find out interesting facts and anecdotes about the lives of the stars. One night, a particularly noteworthy gathering was underway in Holmby Hills. I was standing in the parking lot when a handsome young man in an expensive silk shirt and custom-tailored jeans exited a Maserati with a stunning redhead on his arm.

I realized with a sudden start that it was none other than Sheldon Dickless—a classmate of mine from P.S. 195 in Rego Park, Queens, and a young man universally regarded as a nerd.

Rushing up to him and introducing myself, I said, "Sheldon..."

"Spike," he corrected me.

"All right, Spike. I can't help noticing how much you've changed since those days back in Rego Park. What happened?"

Sheldon looked at me with those blue eyes—once rheumy and bloodshot, now clear and piercing—and said, "The answer is in three words: *Dr. Mildred Sternfricker.*"

Dr. Sternfricker had, from long practice in the Los Angeles community, hit upon a new kind of treatment: *bottom-line therapy.* As she once told me, "It is perfectly true that you can have a $1 million home, a $50,000 car, a diversified stock portfolio, your name on every 'A' list in town, and your choice of sexual partners, and still be severely disturbed.

"But who gives a shit?"

It is this kind of wisdom that formed the bedrock of Dr. Sternfricker's bottom-line therapy. In order to make clear the simple yet invaluable nature of her insights, we have arranged this book informally—one might almost say casually. Don't think of it, then, as a *book*—with that word's forbidding sense of rigor, study, thought. Think of it as a conversation, a chat, a casual exchange, a clearing of the throat—anything to help you realize that what may seem like nothing more than a few simple platitudes is instead a way of life that can lead you to a new understanding of what makes it all worthwhile.

Willie Cashin

1

For $50 an Hour, I'll Be Your Own Best Friend, Plus You Get Lunch

**By Dr. Mildred Sternfricker
with Willie Cashin**

CHAPTER ONE: GETTING THE MESSAGE

It's Saturday night.

You're home.

Home in a tiny apartment.

An apartment you can't afford.

You're eating tuna salad, C & C Cola, and a cookie.

On a tray.

On your bed.

Watching a cheap black and white television set.

No one's called.

You're depressed.

Do you think you're depressed because of some long-dormant guilt?

Do you think you're depressed because you are contemplating the finiteness of life?

If this is what you think, you are not getting the message.

Look around. Look at your room.

Look at your clothes.

Look at your checkbook.

Look at your small black and white television set.

Now you are getting the message.

CHAPTER TWO: THE VALUE OF YOU

So many of us go through our lives never thinking that we are of any value at all.

We learn it from our mothers.

We learn it from our fathers.

We learn it from our sisters.

We learn it from our brothers.

We learn it from our friends.

We learn it from our teachers.

We learn it from our preachers.

I remember a patient who came to me recently and said, "I don't know what to do—I'm of no value."

This man had made a simple but fundamental mistake.

He had failed to take the income from his substantial salary as a motion picture executive and put it to proper use.

No municipal bonds.

No exchange of ordinary income for the steady accumulation of capital assets.

No use of the genuinely compassionate provisions of the Foreign Investment Credit Act of 1977.

Now he was no longer in his position.

Now he was truly a man with no value.

There is a lesson here for all of us.

CHAPTER THREE: HOW TO FEEL BETTER

Many of us believe that we are destined to go through life feeling bad.

This is not true.

I once felt bad all the time.

I was a resident in a big city hospital.

I saw sick people. Wounded people. Hurting people.

All day.

All night.

For $475 a month.

I drove a Dodge.

Used.

Now I see pretty people. Handsome people.

Four hours a day.

When I feel like it.

I make $475 a day.

Before lunch.

I drive a 450 SL.

I feel better.

See?

CHAPTER FOUR: HOW TO DO MORE

Some of my patients who are in the creative world tell me, "Doctor, I just don't have enough time to do the things I want to do."

This is one of those burdens from the past you must clear from your mind.

Consider this book as an example.

When my publisher said, "Dr. Sternfricker, you must write a book for us," I laughed.

"Look at my schedule," I said. "My patients. My tennis. My dinner parties. It is impossible."

Then my publisher said something else. My accountant advises me not to say what it was, but it persuaded me.

I would write a book.

But how?

Then we realized that the solution was right in front of our eyes.

Who says sentences have to be long?

What superstition tells us paragraphs must have lots of sentences?

Is there some rule about how many words must be on a page?

These are hang-ups from our past.

So we got rid of them.

We took responsibility for our own book.

We wrote it our way.

In nine days.

And now I have written a book.

That is how you do more.

CHAPTER FIVE: THE BOTTOM LINE

Many of my patients believe there is no chance that they will ever do what they dream of doing.

Sometimes this is true.

You will probably never play center field for the New York Yankees.

You will probably never run a four-minute mile.

You will probably never climb Mt. Everest.

You will probably never fly a rocket to the moon.

Or Mars.

Or Venus.

Or Jupiter.

(You see? Another chapter is almost done.)

But some things can be done.

Provided you have your own best friend.

Me.

How can I be your own best friend?

Simple.

Let us say, as an example, you are here in Southern California, as a patient of mine was about a year ago.

You are unhappy and depressed.

Why?

Because you were not toilet trained properly?

Because your mother whipped you for playing with yourself?

Nonsense.

You—this patient—was depressed because no one would read her script.

No one would even meet with her.

No one would take her phone calls.

She came to me desperate. Unhappy.

Did I nag her with talk of her past?

No.

Did I spend a year trying to get her to tell me that she liked sex better on her stomach?

No.

Who cares?
I threw a lunch.
Small.
Tasteful.
At Ma Maison.
I invited David Picker.
And Daniel Melnick.
And Tom Mount.
And Dino de Laurentiis.
We had poached salmon.
We had duck Montmorency.
We had fruit and cheese.
We had Mersault.
Seventy-three.
I introduced my patient to David.
And Daniel.
And Tom.
And Dino.
She has four deals lined up.
She's exec on two.
What did I get?
Satisfaction.
Pride.
Half a point on each deal.
Now she is happy.
She is free.
She has taken responsibility for her own life.
She has taken a place in the Colony.

CHAPTER SIX: TAKE A MEETING WITH YOURSELF
How can you decide whether I should be your own best friend?
Take a meeting.
Not with your agent.
Not with your lawyer.
Not with your producer.

Not with a vice-president for programming, prime time.
No.
Take a meeting with yourself.
Put your demands on the table.
What do you want?
75K worth of satisfaction?
Ten percent off the top of guilt-free sex?
Now negotiate.
Is happiness out of the question?
Is your libido on a downhold?
How about maturity?
Will you take an option on pride?
Without exclusivity?
How about play or pay?
After you take a meeting with yourself, call me.
We'll talk.
We'll have lunch.
Maybe I can help.
But that's up to you.
You have to take charge of your own life.
Bel Air or the San Fernando Valley?
Meat loaf or terrine of mallard?
The Honda or the Bugatti?
The Other Korvette's or Giorgio's?
You know better than I what you want.
But I know how to help you get it.
Will it cost you?
Do producers shit on writers?
Is it worth it?
Do writers ball researchers?

ARE YOU QUALIFIED
TO BECOME A PATIENT OF
DR. MILDRED STERNFRICKER?

TAKE THIS SIMPLE QUIZ

After reading this book, many thousands of you are wondering whether you can become a patient of Dr. Sternfricker.

Obviously, Dr. Sternfricker cannot possibly see and treat all of those eager for her special brand of bottom-line therapy.

To weed out the possible patients, Dr. Sternfricker has devised this simple form. Fill it out and mail it with a $250 processing fee to:

Dr. Mildred Sternfricker
Sternfricker Foundation
Charing Cross Rd.
Holmby Hills, Calif. 09056

If you don't hear from Dr. Sternfricker in six weeks, forget it.

Name _____
Address _____
Telephone Number _____
Business Address _____
Business Telephone _____
Position in Business _____
Gross Revenues of Business _____
Adjusted Gross Income of Patient-Applicant _____
Net Worth of Patient-Applicant _____
Names of Six Friends of Patient-Applicant _____
_____
_____
Names of Maitre d's personally known to Patient Applicant _____

List of Symptoms (check if applicable):
- ☐ Vague sense of unease
- ☐ Being followed by aliens
- ☐ Laser beams giving headaches
- ☐ Blood in stool
- ☐ Migraine headaches
- ☐ Guilt over exorbitant sums of money
- ☐ Blocked when rewriting car chases for Aaron Spelling

If she's told you once, she's told you a thousand times...
and here it comes again.

The Lamentation of Eve

Madeline Wyner

Broadside Books
$8.95

The Lamentation of Eve

Madeline Wyner

CHAPTER ONE

<u>Here</u>, Stephanie thought to herself. <u>Here there is peace</u>. To dress without covering her body in clothes defined by their appeal to men.... No need to scrub her face clean, cheeks pinched to shine and glow—the better to find a man.... Here she could eat joyously, feast richly, without a chill of fear that her flesh would thicken, and thereby dull the gleam in the eye of a man.... And, as was happening so often these days, she found herself thinking back, back to the origins of the imprisonment from which she had so recently escaped. Back...back...

CHAPTER TWO

It wasn't easy for Stephanie when she entered the seventh grade at Coolidge Junior High in 1955. She had never been popular with the other children. She always got the best marks in school, and her sense of personal self-worth would not let her hide the fact of her success the way so many other girls did. Stephanie's favorite self-affirmation was to get her test paper back, turn to the others in her class, and say, "Beat you again, morons!" She had never let their petty, bullying tactics destroy her inner sense of strength; when the other kids set fire to her dress, she simply rolled around until it was out.

But in seventh grade, something happened. One day, she noticed that Susan, Betty, and Carole were clustered in the ladies' room, whispering and giggling as they examined a package. Naturally they didn't let Stephanie see what was going on. "Let me see what you're looking at," she requested, "assuming you idiots understand it." They wouldn't, but she got the idea that it was something secret and shameful.

1

Then, a few weeks later, while correcting the history textbook she was studying, Stephanie felt a warm trickle running down her leg. It was red and sticky. She bolted from the classroom and ran home, sobbing, into her mother's arms.

Wanda was in the kitchen, on her hands and knees, scrubbing the heel marks her unemployed, alcoholic, wife-and-child-beating husband had made when Stephanie ran in.

"What's happening to me, Mama?" Stephanie wailed.

"It's the mark of Cain," Wanda replied. "It means you must spend your life in bondage to men. Every month you will bleed and ache, because God made you to be man's servant, to spend your days doing his bidding, to service him sexually no matter how foul or humiliating his demands, to sacrifice every hope of happiness, self-fulfillment, independence, and joy to men, no matter how stupid, dull, or cruel they may be."

"You sure?" said Stephanie.

"Positive," said Wanda.

"Okay," said Stephanie.

The next day, she went to school wearing a very tight sweater, a poodle skirt, and penny loafers, with her hair in a ponytail and her face all made up with lipstick and rouge. She would follow her mother's advice, she had decided, and serve the men in her life as best she could. That day, during a history test, Stephanie tried as hard as she could to think like a boy. When the test came back marked D–, she knew she'd succeeded.

CHAPTER THREE

For the next three years, Stephanie Boar was one of the most popular girls in school. She was treasurer of the student body, captain of the cheerleaders, an officer in the Keen-Teens, and an active figure in the Coolidge Cuties, who sang at all the PTAs. If you had told Stephanie that she was defining herself by male standards. . . if you had told her that she was leading a life that would doom her to bitter ashes for years and years and years. . . if you had told her that every waking moment of her life was a sham and a delusion. . . she probably would have called you a meddling creep. How dearly this would cost her in the years ahead!

Because Stephanie was popular, she began dating the best "socies" in school. There was Biff, captain of the football team, who drooled onto his shirt and ate the pickings of his nose; there was Kenny, president of the student body, who couldn't read; there was Ned, son of the richest man in town, who drove a fancy Corvette and who bought her fancy dinners and expensive candies and flowers. Usually she went out with Ned, for, as Wanda kept telling her, "It's just as easy to fall in love with a rich man as a poor man."

The only trouble was, Ned couldn't keep his hands off her. Oh, it happened with all the boys, Stephanie realized. Every Friday and Saturday night, as she stood in front of the mirror and pulled her sweater tight over her swelling breasts, and tugged the skirt over her youthful hips, smoothing out the wrinkles, and drew on the sheer stockings, and dabbed perfume behind her ears and low on the neck, Stephanie hoped that just this once boys would treat her as a friend. But every time she went out, and slid next to Biff or Kenny or Ned on the front seat, and ran her fingers through their hair, they wanted to...to touch her...there.

All boys were alike, Stephanie realized, but Ned was the most insistent. He seemed somehow older, more experienced than the other boys. Perhaps it was the way he lightly ran his hands over her nipples that gave her this vague sense.

One night, they were parked out by Sluts' Haven, Stephanie's favorite after-movies place. Stephanie had a rigid code of morals for her dates: light kiss the first date, tongue-kissing on the second, dry humping third-to-fifth, with bare tit on the sixth date providing the check at the restaurant came to more than fifteen dollars. But that was as far as it went; Stephanie knew how fast a reputation could get around school.

"Please, Stephanie," Ned was saying, running his hands over her nipples again. They had only had hamburgers ($6.75 plus tip), so Stephanie had kept her brassiere on. But Ned was insistent, and there were strange feelings quivering through her body that she had only felt before when she was alone in her room with her ball point pen.

"I need it bad, Stephanie," Ned said, as sweat poured down his face. "I promise I'll respect you in the morning; I promise I'll only put it in and take it right out; I promise I won't come in you; and I promise, promise not to tell anybody, and I'll buy you a fifteen-dollar dinner every night for two months."

"You sure?" said Stephanie.

As they climbed out of the Corvette and lay on the blanket that Ned kept stored in the trunk, Stephanie's mind was racing. Would it hurt? What would it look like? What was the most expensive dish on the menu at La Maison du Crepes out on Route 51? Then Ned had his clothes off and Stephanie stared at him, naked.

It looked funny—all stiff and wrinkled—like Grandpa Albert at Thanksgiving dinner. Then Ned lay on top of her, and Stephanie felt a sudden, sharp pain...and it was over.

"Wasn't it wonderful, Stephanie?" Ned said. "Of course, you realize I can't ever see you again because, in giving in to my rampant lust, you've proven yourself unworthy of me. Now," he said, hurrying her into the car as she clutched her underpants in her hand, "let's hurry and get you home, so I can drop into the Hog Trough and tell all the guys what we did here tonight."

"But...but," Stephanie said, "you promised me you wouldn't tell anybody."

"I know," said Ned, "but I'm a man, whose rutting lusts—utterly unaccompanied by any sense of tenderness or caring about your own needs, desires, and feelings—include a competitive 'keeping score' sense of sex, which precludes feeling respect for anyone who gives in to what he wants."

"Oh," Stephanie said.

CHAPTER FOUR

For the next two years, Stephanie went all the way with sixty-five of the seventy-two boys in the senior class at Coolidge High. Once Ned had finished telling the guys at the Hog Trough what had happened, no boy would go out with her for less than what she had given Ned. There was Biff, who drooled all over her, and Kenny, who could never read the instructions on the rubber, and others who took her out, bought her hamburgers, jumped on top of her body, and then took her home and never called her again.

Stephanie knew that something was wrong with the way she was living her life, but she couldn't quite put her finger on it. The only thing that saved her was the fact that in her senior year, John Kennedy was elected president. Night after night, as she lay on the back seats of cars, or on the wicker couches of playrooms (so that her rear end looked like twin waffles), she closed her eyes and imagined that the virile young president of the United States was stretched out above her, murmuring into her ear, "Let us begin anew."

After her graduation, Stephanie went off to Indiana Normal College, the only school that would accept her with her boy-pleasing low grades. There, something happened that was to change her life. One evening, during freshman year, Stephanie was waiting in the stacks of the library for Freddie Farmer, her date for the night (Stephanie's reputation had followed her to college; by her own calculations, she would have gone through the entire male student body by February of her freshman year, leaving her three-and-a-half years of total isolation). For some reason or other, Freddie was delayed; to pass the time, Stephanie pulled a book down and idly began leafing through it. The book was <u>A Doll's House</u>.

With mounting excitement, Stephanie began reading the play as fast as she could. This was her life! This was her fate! She was nothing but a doll—a party doll—to satisfy the basest impulses of men! She was an object—a sex object—treated as a giant cloacal presence, without a brain, without a soul, without a future! Now she knew what had been afflicting her so painfully for so long; and she had thought it was herpes simplex.

She heard a rustling sound and put the book in her bag. It was Freddie Farmer.

"Sorry I was late, Stephanie," Freddie said as he began unbuttoning his shirt and tugging down his pants. His member was purple and turgid, like the writing in a bad feminist novel.

"Never mind," said Stephanie. "Everything's changed now. I've discovered my destiny; I've discovered that I will no longer be used as a receptacle, no longer be a simple object for man's lust...."

"See," said Freddie, as he pulled a small box from his pocket, "I've been watching you all semester on campus and I've decided that I love you. So I want you to marry me."

"You sure?" said Stephanie.

CHAPTER FIVE

At first, Stephanie's marriage to Freddie Farmer seemed fine. Freddie was studying veterinary pharmacy, and was spending long hours at the corral learning how to give nose drops to horses and cows. Stephanie was working ten hours a day at the Kresge's soda fountain—she and Freddie dreamed of opening an animal drugstore with a little luncheonette for humans someday—and in her spare time she cooked, cleaned Freddie's dirty clothes, scrubbed the floor, walls, and toilets, cleaned out the furnace, and fixed the pipes. Their sex life seemed to have tailed off shortly after their honeymoon, since Freddie liked to come home, put his feet up, read the papers, and then fall asleep. When Stephanie called her mother to complain, Wanda said the whole thing sounded pretty good to her.

"Remember, dear, you're a woman. Remember how unpopular you were when you were smart and assertive? Now you've got a man; that's all you have a right to expect."

But Stephanie wasn't so sure. Every month or so, she'd find herself returning to <u>A Doll's House</u>, promising herself that if things got too bad, she could always just walk out the door. But then, one morning, she woke up to intense stomach pains and nausea. Freddie was annoyed because it meant he'd have to

5

fix his own coffee and toast, but Stephanie was petrified. It couldn't be...it just couldn't....

"Yessireebob," said Dr. Fagel, the popular animal surgeon at Illinois Normal who doubled as the faculty obstetrician. "I 'spect you'll drop your foal sometime in spring."

"You sure?" said Stephanie.

"Yup," Dr. Fagel said with a big smile. "Gonna be a whole new life for you. Cleaning dirty diapers, and staying up late all night with a wet, crying baby, and getting oatmeal and baby food in your hair, and watching your body turn fat and flaccid so that no one will look at you with anything but extreme disgust, and turning your whole life over to a squalling infant who'll grow into a wretched, ungrateful child who will leave you to grow old and die....Yup," Dr. Fagel said, misty-eyed, "it's a miracle of God."

CHAPTER SIX

When Freddie, Jr., was born, Stephanie's life took on new meaning. Oh, sure, she thought, there were times when she resented the smelly, filthy, squalling bundle of flesh who woke her several times a night and got oatmeal and baby food in her hair and forced her body to turn fat and flaccid so that no one looked at her with anything but extreme disgust and made her a prisoner of his ceaseless demands....

But then there were the other times, when Junior was asleep, after several tablespoonsful of codeine-laced cough medicine. Then Stephanie could put her feet up and read A Doll's House and enjoy the reveries of leaving the little house after lighting several gasoline-soaked rags.

And there were also her friends, the other young mothers whose husbands were graduate students or young instructors at Normal. There was so much to talk about: how to get baby shit out of diapers; how to get oatmeal out of hair; how stupid, unfeeling, and sexually inadequate their husbands were; how empty their lives were; how there seemed to be nothing ahead of them except old age, withering, and death; how to get stubborn stains out of polyester slacks.

"Stephanie," said one of her friends, Monique, "you seem oddly depressed and unhappy. Is anything wrong?"

"Not really," said Stephanie. "I wake up, brush my teeth, change Junior's diapers, run into the bathroom and vomit my guts up for five minutes, then start coffee...."

"Hmmm," said Monique. "I could have sworn something was out of sorts with you. Have you ever thought of…of seeing a psychiatrist? I mean, it's someone to talk with to get your problems out in the open."

Two days later, Stephanie was lying on the couch of Dr. Ophelia Nelson; she'd chosen a woman because no man had ever listened to her seriously. A woman, she knew, would be able to deal with her frustrations, help her to shape a life of meaning and purpose. It was so helpful to be able to talk of her life without the constant interruptions of husband and son. How the time flew.…

"So then, Doctor, I began feeling…this <u>incredible</u> sense of loss and helplessness. No one would <u>listen</u> to me, no one would face my complaints and realize that my entire life had been defined by male expectations and demands, how there was no chance to express my own capacities, to be treated as a serious individual.…Doctor?…Doctor?…"

"Huh?! Whazza?…Go on, go on," Dr. Nelson said.

CHAPTER SEVEN

<u>Here</u>, Stephanie thought, <u>here there was peace</u>. At the Juno Institute for Health, there were no men at all to disturb her contemplation. Here, far from the demands of Freddie and Junior and the manager at Kresge's, here Stephanie could find that sense of individual pride she had for so long denied herself.

And there was more.… One day, Dr. Nelson came into her room—careful to preserve formality by knocking on the door, even though the rubber padding gave off no sound—and brought with her a smartly-dressed woman who simply radiated assurance and a sense of self-worth.

"Stephanie," said Dr. Nelson, "this is Diane Fentress, of Grisette Press. She'd very much like to hear your story."

<u>Here they listen</u>, Stephanie thought, as she leisurely spun out her story of pride and worth crushed under the heel of male definition and domination, of the demands of sexual servility, of the bonds of motherhood without satisfaction.

"And every day, every day, cleaning the shit out of the diapers, and washing, and cooking with no money for food.…Ms. Fentress?…Ms. Fentress?…"

"Huh?! Whazza?…Go on, go on," Diane said.

"Didn't I tell you she was perfect?" said Dr. Nelson.

"You've done it again, Doc," said Diane with a broad smile. She put her arm around Stephanie. "Honey," Diane said, "get yourself a typewriter and an agent. Then put every word of this down as fast as you can. You're about to be a very happy woman."

"You sure?" said Stephanie.

Poor, Schmoor!

Leo Levanter

A loving look back at a city boyhood in a simpler America.

Tsouris Press
For you, $8.75

You know, it amazes me. It truly does. Everywhere I go I hear people complaining about their lives. The appliances that don't work...the fancy houses in the suburbs that need repairing...the car that's always in the shop.

And I think to myself, Leo, how come when you were a kid on Delancey Street, in a special place in New York called the Lower East Side, you never heard complaints? Because to us, really, I'm not kidding, the Lower East Side was a little strip of heaven that God put right here on earth.

And then I remember a special bit of wisdom that a great teacher, what we of the Jewish faith call a *chraine,* told me when I was a little boy attending religious school, or as we call it, *blechkas.* The *chraine* looked at me with those wide eyes of his, and breathed on me with a breath that was said to have killed three horses, and intoned, "My son, when you sit in a wretched hut gnawing on a crust of bread, you do not know that in the house of the landlord, the chicken soup is cold."

Were we poor back then, growing up in a new country, with a new language and a new society? As my people would say, *"Oy!"*

One day my father—may God rest his poor soul—came into our fifth story hovel in a broken-down tenement, hauling his pushcart behind him. (We were so poor, my father couldn't afford the two cents a month to park his pushcart in the shed owned by McGonigle the Mick; every night he had to drag his cart up all five flights of stairs.)

"Shpilkus the Scholar came by today," my father said. "He told me that in America they have something they call the 'Protestant work ethic.' I said to him, 'Shpilkus, I already know from the Protestant work ethic. The Jews work sixteen hours a day so the Protestants can send their children to Princeton to study ethics.'"

Even in these conditions, my father could see that God wasn't really punishing us, just testing us with a series of practical jokes. And when my father was on his deathbed, a broken, emaciated man at thirty-seven, and a hospital official came into the charity ward and said, "Mrs. Levanter, if your husband is still alive by the morning, we're going to have to throw him into the street since the bill hasn't been paid," my father, with his last breath,

1

looked up at the sky, smiled, winked broadly, and gasped, "Okay, okay, I get it, I get it."

Believe me, with medicine like my people's laughter, disease doesn't stand a chance.

Humor, I always say, is laughter's ambassador to the world. It needs no passport, no identification, no working papers. I remember in 1919, when the worldwide influenza epidemic ravaged millions around the world. When it came to New York, like any tourist looking for an interesting experience, it came to the Lower East Side, where we lived nine, ten, twelve to a room—often sleeping suspended from hooks in the wall.

So swiftly did this disease proliferate in such circumstances that my Tante Gretl, watching her family collapse before her eyes, addressed a scornful remark to the influenza, saying, "Nu, don't get up, Mr. Virus—we'll spread your germs *for* you." I wish she had lived to hear the laughter that line got years later at Grossinger's.

Anyway, in the middle of this epidemic, my five-year-old brother was walking down Mott Street on a particularly fetid day; bodies of the dead and dying were draped over pushcarts like suits on sale. It was so hot, so steaming, that even the animals and insects couldn't bear it. A fly began falling out of the air, and dropped dead right at my brother's feet. He pointed with a bony finger and, with fevered eyes, smiled and said, "Leo! Leo! The flies are dropping like people!"

Oh, to hear that kind of humor today....

With such a life, family discipline was important. In the neighborhood where I grew up, poppa ruled the roost. Now, of course, he's just chicken....But seriously, in those days, when a child misbehaved, his mother would intone the dreaded words, "Wait till your father gets home!" Nowadays, when poppa gets home, he shares a joint with his kid...in those days, he dislocated one.

The kids at school used to tell stories about whose poppa was the worst. Remember? One day Shlomo came into school with a big smile on his face; three of his teeth were gone, and his cheek looked like raw hamburger.

"Boy, when my pop found out I'd played hooky yesterday, you know what he did? He dragged me into the cellar, tied me to a pickle barrel, took a big piece of wood, and beat me for a half hour. We told the emergency room I fell off a truck."

Well, the next day Knadlech came to school with his entire body wrapped in bandages. He had to hop for six blocks.

"When my pop found out I'd been smoking butts, you know what he did? He pulled me by the hair into the alley, tied me to a drainpipe, picked up an iron crowbar, and beat me until the blood ran from both ears and my nose. Then he said, 'That was a *warning.*'"

Two days later, we're in the schoolyard when the junk wagon pulls up alongside of school. Samuel's father owns the junkyard, and every day Sammy would come to school riding the wagon. Only this day, Sammy's father picks up a bundle wrapped up in burlap and drops it into the schoolyard. Attached to the bag is a note:

See how tough my pop is? I'm dead inside the bag!—Sammy

You see, as the Bible says, "He that loveth well, chastiseth well." Believe you me, in that neighborhood, there was plenty of love.

You know the old expression, "Work till you drop"? In my old neighborhood, that was no figure of speech. Jobs were hard to come by, and you took what you could get. But no matter how fast the sewing machines spun, no matter how heavy the garments were, there was always time for a rueful smile and a happy word that would somehow make the day and night go a little bit faster.

One day, two workers met on the street, each one looking frailer and more anemic than the other. Now these two workers always tried to outdo each other with their tales of woe—an ancient Jewish tradition called *grechtnech*.

"Morris," says the first one. "You can't believe what a life I lead. The doctor at the clinic figured out that every day, my family and I need 5,000 of those what-you-call vitamins just to live; but with what that *momser* Glickstein pays me, I can only afford 5,100. I tell you, if things get any worse, my family will starve."

"You think *you* got trouble," says Morris. "My family also needs 5,000 of those vitamins a day. But the thief I work for, Trelbaum—may his soul burn in hell—he pays me so little I can only afford 4,500. Every single day we're losing 500 vitamins."

"But Morris," says the first one. "How do you survive?"

Morris shrugs and says, "Volume."

Everywhere I go, people come up to me and say, "Leo, I must tell you something my grandmother used to say to me." Or, "Leo, did your child ever say this to you?" Over the years, I have collected thousands of these phrases, which my people call *klishays*. I have shared some of these with you in the past. Permit me to indulge myself again, for I have come to believe that there can be more wisdom, more laughter, more tears, more humanity in the simple phrase of a gnarled old woman with varicose veins and a tumor spreading through her body like a forest fire in Los Angeles than in a thousand government studies. Believe me, sometimes I think we would be a lot better off if we changed the Department of HEW to mean Hugging, Eating, and Wisdom.

3

POOR, SCHMOOR!

Anyway, here are some of my favorites, and I hope they will become some favorites of yours:

- If God had wanted you to be happy, he wouldn't have given you a congenital heart disorder.
- Death is God's way of telling you not to be such a wise guy.
- How come I pay so much for *health* insurance, but I still get *sick*?
- With all the fancy scientists in the world, why can't they build just once a nuclear *balm*?
- I have a condominium in Miami, a diversified stock portfolio, and a Buick, but when I realize I'll be dead in a few years, it still makes me throw up.
- My son-in-law figured out a way to make ends meet; he walks around with his head up his ass.

Other Beloved Books by Leo Levanter

Jokes for the Potty: Toilet Training Through Laughter
Who Knew from the Ghetto?
Take My Life, Please
If You Don't Go to Shul on Friday, You'll Get a Lot Worse Than Saturday Night Fever
These Yids Today: A Loving, Laughing Look at Contemporary American Judaism

Credits

Art Direction and Design: *Peter Kleinman*
Photography: *Phil Koenig*
Additional Photography: *Peter DeFrancis*
Associate Art Director: *Alison Antonoff*
Art Associate: *"Ciene" Delores Moffett*
Copy Editor: *Louise Gikow*
Props: *Marguerite Lobiak*
Research: *Susan Rosenthal*

Cover.. *sculpture by Carter Jones*

The Curse of Satan's Harvest...................... *photograph by Phil Koenig, retouched by Bob Rakita*

Get Out of My Way or I'll Kill You.................... *cover by Terry McGee, illustrations by Jack Medoff*

The Gilt-Edged Mind Rapers..*illustrated by Bob Larkin*

Simply...Picasso.....................................*photographed by Pedar Ness, cover art by Neal Adams*

How Did I Get Here?..*illustrated by Rhonda Klapper*

Love's Tormenting Itch...*illustrated by Mara McAfee*

The Cooking of Provincial New Jersey.................*photographed by Ron Harris and Jerry Friedman*

The Book of Fings...*illustrated by Randy Enos*

For $50 an Hour, I'll Be Your Own Best Friend................................*designed by Alison Antonoff*

The Lamentation of Eve..*illustrated by Randy Enos*

Poor, Schmoor!...*designed by Alison Antonoff*

Many thanks to *John Weidman, and to models Ron Barrett, Henry Ferrentino, Jeff Greenfield, Sean Kelly, Sandra Richman, Martin Rosenblatt, Anita Russell, Robin Schwartz, C. Alexander Strait, Dennis Vestunis, Alan Wellikoff, Bill Workman.*

Also, thanks to *Au Natural, Pete's Tavern, the Hotel Algonquin, Brooks Van Horne, Kenmore Leasing, Encore Studios, De Ray Binding, and The Color Wheel.*